Reproduction, Sex, and Preparation for Marriage

LAWRENCE Q. CRAWLEY
JAMES L. MALFETTI
ERNEST I. STEWART
NINI VAS DIAS

prentice-hall, inc., englewood cliffs, new jersey

Current printing (last digit):

12   11   10   9   8   7

PRENTICE-HALL INTERNATIONAL, INC., *London*
PRENTICE-HALL OF AUSTRALIA, PTY., LTD., *Sydney*
PRENTICE-HALL OF CANADA, LTD., *Toronto*
PRENTICE-HALL OF INDIA (PRIVATE) LTD., *New Delhi*
PRENTICE-HALL OF JAPAN, INC., *Tokyo*

Library of Congress Catalog Card Number: 64-23237

Printed in the United States of America

C-77392C
C-77391P

preface

SEX AND REPRODUCTION are of lively interest to young adults. This book presents facts and clinical insights to supplement interest with knowledge and a sense of perspective.

There was nothing hypothetical about the selection of subject matter. It was chosen from the interests college students have shown and from the questions and problems of persons who have sought premarital and postmarital advice and counseling from us. It is discussed to the depth that seemed necessary to satisfy those raising the question or experiencing the problem. For those who wish additional information about specific subjects, the bibliography will be helpful.

Facts of reproductive anatomy and physiology are discussed in Chapter One. We believe that facts should come first, for one's opinions and decisions about sexual matters should be supported and guided by the most current facts wherever possible. The knowledge possessed by the average adolescent and young adult regarding the so-called "facts of life" is inadequate by almost any standard. Formal education in general has been evasive. The young adult wants to know about his own reproductive anatomy and physiology, and about that of the opposite sex. He wants to know about the physical aspects of mating—both for the knowledge itself and for its eventual application in his own life.

He also wants to know about conception, prenatal development, and birth, and these are discussed in Chapter Two. As he comes to understand the magnitude, marvel, and intricacies of reproduction, he is likely to develop a responsible attitude toward sex in regard to himself as well as the opposite sex. He is ready for a discussion of premarital sexual conduct, and the role of sex and love in courtship and marriage, which follows in later chapters. He should thereby be better prepared to assume the responsibilities that accompany his sexual activities.

The sex life of the unmarried young adult poses a social problem which society has largely ignored, primarily because it has no workable and acceptable answer. Chapter Three is concerned with this problem as well as with the factors involved in psychosexual development, and considerations and guideposts for sexual conduct. From society's point of view the most desirable condition for sexual expression is marriage, but unfortunately in our culture there is little identity between biological readiness for sexual expression and readiness for marriage. Although continence until marriage has been the expressed ideal, it is apparently too much to expect of most people. They seek some source of sexual outlet. Among young adults the most common expression is masturbation. Worry over this and other sexual experiences, or the desire for such experiences, produces fear, tension, a sense of guilt.

Young people of this generation have more opportunity than ever before for sexual intercourse. Three controlling fears of the past—social disgrace, disease, and pregnancy—have been reduced by new freedom and knowledge. Modern education, which teaches independence and freedom of action, has largely eliminated the chaperon. Automobiles enable young people to travel great distances quickly and reduce the effectiveness of family and community supervision. The automobile itself offers increased opportunities for sexual intimacy. As more and more external authority is removed, young people must assume more and more responsibility for their own patterns of sexual conduct. They seek and need help in reaching standards.

Sex and love are brought to fulfillment in marriage. More than nine of every ten Americans marry, and the majority do so by or in their early twenties. Selecting a spouse was a fairly simple matter for earlier generations. A young man became engaged to a young lady who lived nearby. They probably had similar religious, social and educational backgrounds, and many of the same interests, and had known each other and their respective families most of their lives. Today, however, mobile populations, changing socioeconomic circumstances, and a faster tempo of living have reduced the likelihood that couples contemplating marriage will have known each other well. They recognize the desirability of learning more about each other and their potential for happiness together in marriage, and want assistance in this investigation. Chapter Four discusses the major factors of concern in preparation for marriage.

Young adults thinking about marriage are always interested in the role of sex. They hear much about incompatibility and wonder how it can be tested for and guarded against. Sex can assume a disproportionate weight in evaluating the individual, and may even be equated with the total individual. Many young men think of "nice" girls or "sexy" girls and find it difficult to believe that one girl can be both. Yet they recognize that the girls they marry should be both. Young people need help in learning the role of sex in total personality; they need to understand total relationships as opposed to sex as an end in itself.

The book concerns itself primarily with premarital sexuality; less with the specific role of sex in marriage. It most frequently refers to and discusses the usual or "normal" situations or conditions of sex and reproduction to the relative neglect of the exceptions and pathologies. This sequence of subject matter has been tried and found practicable in the undergraduate men's college of Columbia University. Toward the end of improving readability, a technical word used for the first time is usually in parentheses, and preceded by a descriptive phrase. Subsequently, the technical word is used alone.

There are many essential questions in matters of sex for which no direct or final answers are forthcoming. The authors attempt a clear and factual discussion, but some opinion inevitably creeps into books of this nature. The authors leave decisions regarding behavior to the best judgment of the reader, in the hope that he may consider carefully and seek advice of those whose competence and wisdom he respects.

acknowledgments

The authors wish to acknowledge permission granted for use of the following illustrations:

Figure 4, p. 23, from Tampax Incorporated.

Figure 5, p. 28, from *Anatomy of the Human Body* by Henry Gray, 27th ed., 1959, by permission of Lea & Febiger.

Figure 6, p. 32, and Figure 8, p. 38, from the *Ciba Collection of Medical Illustrations* by Frank H. Netter, M.D., Copyright CIBA Pharmaceutical Company.

Figure 7, p. 35, Figures 16, 17, and 18, p. 65, and Figure 22, p. 77, reproduced with permission from *A Baby is Born*, published by Maternity Center Association, New York City.

Figure 24, p. 175, from *Modern Methods for the Control of Conception* by permission of Ortho Pharmaceutical Corporation.

contents

the roles of
male and female in reproduction

HUMAN LIFE BEGINS when a sperm cell and an egg cell unite. The sperm cell develops within the father, the egg cell within the mother. The union takes place within the reproductive tract of the mother after sexual intercourse. This in essence is the story of human reproduction.

Sex, always related to reproduction, also exists apart from it. The meaning of sex ranges from the bodily differences between male and female to the complex drive responsible for life itself and for many of its pleasures and problems. We will begin our discussion of reproduction and sex with the bodily differences between male and female. Sex in this sense is fixed at the instant the sperm and egg cells unite (*conception*).

bodily differences between the sexes

In every sperm and egg cell there are twenty-three microscopically small bodies (*chromosomes*) which constitute the principal working machinery of heredity, including the determination of sex. All egg cells have similar "sex" chromosomes (x). Half of the sperm cells have one *small* "sex" chromosome (y) and the other half have an x similar to that of the egg cell. If a sperm cell with a y chromo-

1

some fertilizes an egg cell, the individual is male (xy), otherwise it is female (xx). This fact has led some to conclude that the father determines the sex of the child.

From fertilization on, sexual characteristics develop, but it takes some time before differences become apparent. The external genitals are identical in the two sexes during the early stages of life. Not until well along in the third month after conception do small projections on the outer surface of the body begin to undergo changes that make it possible to distinguish male and female.

However, as early as the seventh week after fertilization, both male and female hormones are being produced by the rudimentary sex glands of each sex. This dual production continues throughout a lifetime with periodic changes in the balance. A man usually produces a heavy preponderance of male hormones, a woman much more of the female. It is still unknown whether hormonal differences in the male and female glands develop first, and then cause the sex organs and systems to grow differently, or whether differences in the male and female cells directly produce both hormonal differences and those in the sex organs and systems as a whole.

At the seventh month after conception, the sex glands (*testes*) of the male embryo usually descend into the pouch (*scrotum*) prepared to contain them, and the female sex glands (*ovaries*) take their position in the lower abdomen (*pelvis*). At that time all the principal details of the male and female organs are complete. From then until birth, change in sex organs is limited to growth and refinement.

When the male is born, he already has in his testes all the germinal tissue out of which billions of sperms will eventually be produced. It is not until he is about fourteen to fifteen years old, however, that sperm production (*spermatogenesis*) actually begins.

The female is born with many thousands of eggs in her ovaries. However, only 300 to 400 of these will be available for fertilization —one egg about every twenty-eight days from approximately the fourteenth to the forty-fifth year.

But before the male and female are biologically capable (*puberty*) of creating children (*procreating*) many influences will shape their readiness for and attitudes toward sexual expression and each other. Some of these influences will have biological roots in the small chromosome in the male. Others will have roots in family and other social attitudes toward sexual expression and the roles of men and women.

Aside from differences in sex systems and genitals, the male and female are biologically distinct in other ways. The male embryo develops more slowly; the lag continues through birth to adolescence. Sexually and physically, the girl is ahead. This may account partially for girls' interest in boys before boys' interest in girls. Male embryo losses are heavier, and males are less resistant to death and disease throughout life. The male suffers "color-blindness" and baldness to a far greater extent than the female; statistically, women outlive men by about seven years. Muscle and skeletal patterns are also dissimilar. Girls throw and run differently, which helps to explain why they often play or maintain spectator interest in different games.

social and attitudinal sex differences

Once a boy has passed the pail and shovel stage, his role as a male is made clear to him. Footballs, hammers, guns are acceptable toys, but a doll carriage is not. His play and his interests are preparing him to be like his father—someone who earns the money, takes the lead in the family, but who does not keep house, cry, or act like a "sissy."

When he goes to school, he is encouraged to be on his own, to enjoy rough and ready bodily contacts, and to settle differences through physical strength. In general, he has a freer attitude toward his body and its functions. Boys undress before each other and go naked with healthy abandon and pleasure. Urinating openly is common, and so are competitive games like seeing who can urinate farthest. In many ways a boy is more open about sex than his sister and other girls. Because of the nature of the male organs he is proud of them, whereas girls may have feelings of inadequacy and disappointment about theirs.

Very early a girl is warned about the dangers and consequences of associating with men. To a greater extent than a boy, she is warned to keep away from strangers. There is a fear that she may be seduced or violated sexually and lose her virginity. Girls are encouraged to tend dolls and to perform housewifely duties in miniature. They are told to behave like "young ladies," as opposed to the less attractive "tomboy."

Later, the girl's parents may acquaint her with the facts of life —themselves or through some other source. A good many girls have already sought and obtained information for themselves, sometimes in distorted and misleading form. Frequently it is through girls a few years older, or perhaps the subject has been discussed in class. The parents, nevertheless, should wish to be sure that she is clear on several important points—what to do when boys make sexual advances and what it means to be pregnant and unmarried. Although some parents have an adequate knowledge of reproduction, too many fear an unwanted pregnancy for the girl so much that they are more successful in communicating fear than facts—indeed so successful that the girl may carry this fear into marriage. Parental anxiety about sex may influence a daughter's values and bring them into conflict with her desire to be attractive, even seductive. This antagonism may be heightened by our society's emphasis on physical and sexual attributes.

The boy may also have a talk about sex with someone. The talk is usually more cursory than that given to the girl. He may be warned about the need to "protect" himself against venereal disease, and about causing a girl to become pregnant. Often he is simply warned of the "dangers" of masturbation. He too may suffer great anxiety—about his active phantasy sex thoughts and wish for sexual outlets and his unresolved internal conflicts about what is right and wrong. Helping these young people probably lies in nullifying the extremes with a balanced outlook. A full discussion of psychosexual development will be found in Chapter Three. But now let us examine the physical structure of the sexual organs.

male reproductive system

Testes

The testes are in the scrotum which keeps them at a constant temperature with the aid of a muscle (cremaster) which expands and contracts. The normal testicular temperature is about one degree lower than the body temperature. Males will notice that in cold water the scrotum contracts, holding the testes closer to the body for increased warmth, but relaxes to decrease the amount of body heat reaching the testes in warm water. The testes are sensitive to pain and injury, and prolonged increases in temperature of two or three degrees (as in fever) can temporarily interfere with sperm production. It is unlikely, however, that the hot baths men take as a contraceptive technique in some countries are at all effective— they would have to be taken longer and hotter than is practical. When a male is troubled by low fertility, however, he is sometimes advised not to wear tight underwear. Holding the testes close to the heat of the body may further impede already poor or inadequate sperm production.

Seminiferous Tubules

Within the two testes are small tubes (*seminiferous tubules*) in which sperm cells are produced. Each testis has 300 to 600 of these tubes, which are between one and three feet in length. The aggregate length is almost half a mile.

Sperm Cells

The walls of the seminiferous tubules are lined with germinal tissue in a continuous process of maturation (*spermatogenesis*) whereby the original twenty-three pairs of chromosomes is halved, leaving each sperm cell twenty-three single chromosomes. Although the germinal tissue is in the tubules from birth, spermatogenesis does not occur until puberty. In fact, the appearance of sperm cells is one criterion of puberty in the male. Nothing can be done to hasten the maturation and appearance of sperm cells. Young men sometimes precipitate a climax (*orgasm* and *ejaculation*) by manipulating the penis, or, during sleep, experience an exciting sexual dream ("wet dream") and ejaculate a fluid through the penis as a result of it, but until sperm cells appear in the ejaculate, a male has not biologically reached puberty.

Once begun, the production of sperm cells continues throughout most of the life of the male. In the same way that many cells grow from one to form the individual, millions of germ cells are manufactured from time to time, and can be thrown off without decreasing the reserve stock. Endless billions of sperm can continue to be discharged from a man's body, and the original tissue of germ

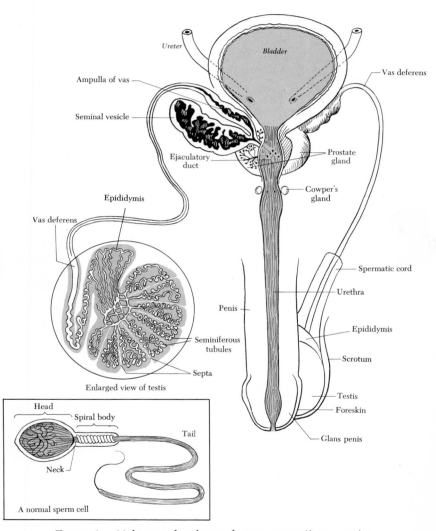

FIGURE 1.   *Male genital and reproductive organs (front view).*

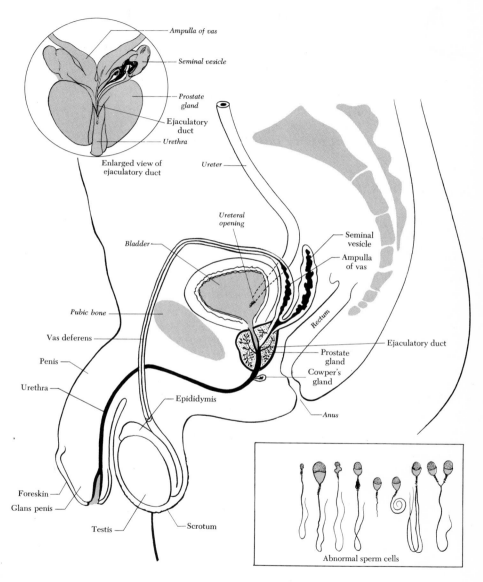

Ampulla of vas

Seminal vesicle

Prostate gland

Ejaculatory duct

Urethra

Enlarged view of ejaculatory duct

Ureter

Ureteral opening

Bladder

Seminal vesicle

Ampulla of vas

Pubic bone

Rectum

Vas deferens

Ejaculatory duct

Penis

Prostate gland

Cowper's gland

Urethra

Epididymis

Anus

Foreskin

Glans penis

Testis

Scrotum

Abnormal sperm cells

Male genital and reproductive organs (side view).

cells will still be there to provide more—so long as the reproductive machinery functions and the body can supply the material out of which to make them. It is groundless to worry over misuse of "seed" as a youth for fear that it may be "used up" before marriage. Barring disease, it is unlikely the male will run out until a very old age. The sperm count in the ejaculate does diminish temporarily after frequent sexual outlet, but the motility of the sperm remains unimpaired. The male experiences no sharp decline in reproductive power comparable to the menopause in the female. After about seventy, the seminiferous tubules begin to thicken, with the resultant decline in sperm production, but male fertility has been authenticated to the age of ninety-four.

While sperm cells are produced in astronomical numbers, only one is used in fertilization. During sexual intercourse 200 to 500 million (occasionally over a billion) are discharged. Although this seems extravagant, it may be good planning—the likelihood of conception is directly related to the abundance of sperm. Sperm cells are infinitesimally small. Two thousand five hundred million—as many as were needed to father all the people in the world today—could easily be contained in a small thimble.

A sperm cell is divided into a head, neck, and tail. The head contains the chromosomes, or hereditary material; the tail develops a whip-like motion which moves the sperm cell along.

Epididymis

When the sperm cell has been formed (twenty-three single chromosomes), it makes its way from the walls to the center of the seminiferous tubules. Contractions (*peristalsis*) of the tubules move the sperm cells forward to a maturation chamber (*epididymis*) which forms a mass over the back and upper part of each testis. Each epididymis measures only two inches in length, but contains a tube twenty feet long. The sperm cells are retained in these tubes perhaps as long as six weeks, while further ripening takes place. The epididymis also serves as a selection chamber, weeding out by absorption those sperm cells less well equipped for fertilization and for transmitting hereditary loads. But normal cells perish here as well. Sperm cells absorb nourishment from the lining membrane, and those crowded to the center, away from the lining, are less likely to survive.

Male Hormone

In addition to the development of sperm cells, another function of the testes is the production of the male hormone (*testosterone*) which is largely responsible for the male sex drive and for such secondary sex characteristics as deepening of the voice and appearance of beard and chest and pubic hair. This hormone is produced in the interstitial cells of the testes and secreted directly into the bloodstream. Only very small quantities of it are found in the male discharge (*semen*). The female hormone (*estrogen*) is also manufactured in the testes, and is always present in the male system in varying quantities. Male and female sex hormones are present in both sexes. In the female, estrogen predominates; in the male, testosterone is normally in greater concentration.

Castration

Removing the testes (*castration*) destroys a male's ability to produce sperm cells, but he may still engage in sexual intercourse with ejaculation. Most of his production of testosterone will also be lost, but small amounts will be manufactured by other glands, the adrenal, for example. If he is castrated before puberty, he will not develop the normal male secondary sex characteristics like growth of a beard and deepening of the voice. At one time choir boys, called castrati, had their soprano or contralto voices preserved this way. Castration after puberty usually does not influence secondary sex characteristics. More testosterone is needed to establish the characteristics than to maintain them. If one testis is removed, the effect on fertility is proportional to the sperm-producing ability of the remaining gland. If the remaining testis is normal, fertility will be good and hormone production will be adequate for normal development.

Disease

Several conditions can cause inability to produce sperm cells. As far as is known, mumps has no injurious effect on the testes of the male before puberty, but mumps after puberty can be complicated by a painful swelling of one or both testes, with possible shrinkage, atrophy, and a considerable or total impairment of spermatogenesis. In less severe cases there may be only a slight decrease in the number of sperm, and some loss of motility.

Undescended Testicles

If the testes do not descend by puberty, sperm-producing ability will be seriously impaired because of the higher temperature of the body. To avoid this impairment glandular injections are given or an operation performed to assist the descent of the testes into the scrotum when the boy is about eight or nine years old. In those cases in which the testes have not descended by puberty the male hormone (testosterone) will still be produced and absorbed internally. The secondary sex characteristics, therefore, will not be affected.

Vas Deferens

The sperms leaving the testis through the epididymis empty into a pin-sized channel within a tube (vas deferens) fifteen to eighteen inches long, which passes upward and over the brim of the pelvis and enters the lower part of the abdomen. The walls of the vas are well developed muscular layers capable of powerful contraction (peristalsis) and lined with little hair-like projections (cilia). Since the sperm at this time is not entirely capable of propelling itself, the contractions and cilia may assist in moving it along.

Male Sterilization

The vasa deferentia are the tubes which are tied off or cut in a male sterilization operation. Since the tubes pass just beneath the skin of the scrotum, the operation can be performed in minutes under local anesthesia. The operation precludes the passage of sperm, and consequently the possibility of fertilization, but it in no way affects the male's sex drive, his ability to have sexual relations and ejaculate, or his secondary sex characteristics. The testes remain intact and the testosterone that they secrete is absorbed directly into the blood system. The testes continue to produce sperm cells which live, die, and are absorbed in the blocked vas.

In spite of the simplicity of this operation and the relatively complex nature of sterilization for the female, most couples faced with the definite need for one to be sterilized decide that it is to be the woman. Much has been written about the concern of the woman when she faces the loss of her ability to have children, but the man seems at least equally concerned about his own loss. There is a close tie between the male's ego strength, his sexual potency, and his ability to fertilize.

In addition to serving as a passageway for the sperms the vas acts as a storage organ particularly at the broad end (*ampulla*) where it is joined by a small canal leading from a little saclike structure (*seminal vesicle*).

Seminal Vesicle

The seminal vesicle, a gland about two inches long, secretes a substance which the sperm cell converts into energy for movement by the whiplash motion of its tail. It is only after contact with this secretion that the sperm cell is capable of appreciable locomotion of its own. The seminal vesicle is prepared to function at birth, but does not begin secretory activity until puberty. The place at which the canal from the vesicle unites with the ampulla of the vas and the urethra is known as the ejaculatory duct.

Urethra

The male urethra has a twofold function—the elimination of urine from the bladder and the transmission of sperm cells through the erect penis to the exterior of the body. There is rarely danger of simultaneous functioning. A small valvelike structure (*bladder sphincter*) closes the exit of the bladder and prevents the escape of urine during ejaculation, and the openings of the vas close during urination.

Prostate

The ejaculatory ducts and the portion of the urethra into which they empty are surrounded by a glandular mass (*prostate*) made up of thirty to forty small glands that open into the urethra. These glands produce a secretion, which, like that of the seminal vesicles, stimulates and facilitates the motility of sperm cells. This secretion is alkaline and serves as a buffer in counteracting the acid condition of the urethra of the male and of the vagina in which the sperm are deposited to accomplish fertilization. Sperm cells are readily killed by acid like that normally present in vaginal fluid.

The prostate is a common site for infection in young men and for enlargement and cancer in older men. Unfortunately, as it grows larger or swells it can interfere with urination, which becomes quite painful and difficult. Many older men must have the prostate removed. Its functions are somewhat duplicated and expanded by those of the seminal vesicles, and its removal normally does not interfere with sexual potency or fertility.

Penis

The penis is variable in size, but in the relaxed state averages three inches in length and one and one-quarter inches in diameter. It is composed largely of the urethra surrounded by muscles and by spongy tissue containing a great number of blood vessels. Under sexual excitement these vessels fill with blood and become greatly enlarged, causing the penis to stiffen and to protrude from the body at an upward angle (*erection*). The erect penis averages six inches in length and one and one-half inches in diameter. The size of sexual organs is not very important to satisfactory sexual relations. The flaccid penis may vary in size, but erection is a great equalizer in that the relative increase in size is greater for smaller penises than for larger. More important by far than organ size are attitudes relating to the genitals and to the sex act. Sexual relations should express one's ability to love and to be loved as a whole person, not as a sex organ or a sex symbol.

Circumcision

The conelike head of the penis (*glans*) is partially covered by the foreskin (*prepuce*). Circumcision cuts the foreskin back to behind the ridge of the glans. This is performed primarily for hygienic reasons as the glans sheds cells which form a pastelike substance (*smegma*) often irritating to the foreskin and glans if not regularly washed away. Circumcision is generally performed about the fifth to eighth day after birth, but sometimes later on in life, especially if the foreskin interferes with erection at that time. The presence of the foreskin in no way influences the pleasure in the sex act, for during erection the foreskin slides over and behind the glans. Occasionally a man who has not been circumcised is troubled with premature ejaculation (before the sex act has gone far enough to satisfy the woman). This condition may be due in part to an increased sensitivity of the head of the penis. Most cases of premature ejaculation, however, seem to be caused psychologically.

Cowper's Glands

Cowper's glands, each about the size of a pea, are situated internally at the base of the penis. During sexual excitement they secrete an alkaline fluid (*pre-ejaculatory fluid*) which tends to neutralize acidity in the urethra and lubricates the urethra for passage of the semen (sperm cells plus secretions). The fluid looks like lime water, and can be observed at the tip of the glans during sexual excitement previous to ejaculation. It may contain a small number of sperm cells, making fertilization possible, but not probable, through resting the penis in the vagina without ejaculation during foreplay or using a contraceptive technique known as withdrawal. This involves withdrawing the penis from the vagina at the last moment so that ejaculation occurs externally. The withdrawal method is discussed more fully in Chapter Four.

Ejaculation

From puberty until advanced age, sperm cells are manufactured continuously for discharge from the body. In sexual play, after the penis has become erect, increasing stimuli produce a period of excitement and pleasure which results in a spasm of muscles in the genital area. At the height of this feeling, the ejaculatory ducts open simultaneously releasing fluids from the seminal vesicles and prostate, and sperm from the epididymides, ampullae of the vas, and other storage places. The muscles of the penis and others in the area contract to propel the semen through the urethra. Ejaculation takes place in a series of spurts, the first being the greatest in volume and containing the largest number of sperm cells. The total ejaculate normally contains between 200 to 500 million sperm cells within a teaspoon of fluid, but smaller or larger amounts are common.

When discharged from the body, the sperm cells become highly active, self-sustaining organisms with the unique facility for continuing life independent of a direct connection with their parent tissues. Except for the occasional sperm cell that is successful in fertilizing an egg, most die a few hours after ejaculation. Those that make their way into the female reproductive system sometimes live twenty-four to forty-eight hours or longer, but by far the greatest number perish in the vagina. It is now well established that sperm must pass through almost the entire length of the female tract to fertilize the egg. They are thought to move an inch in eight minutes, and only the most active and normal succeed in this long and rigorous journey.

female reproductive system

Ovaries

A woman has two ovaries which lie deep in the pelvis, below and to each side of the navel (*umbilicus*). They are slightly flattened, oval bodies about one and one-half inches long, one inch wide, and three-quarters of an inch thick, made up of glandular tissue and tiny egg sacs (*follicles*).

Egg Cells

At birth, the female has about 50,000 or more follicles in each ovary, but comparatively few ever become active. The eggs within them have already undergone a special type of reduction division and have twenty-three single chromosomes. Unlike sperm cells, they are not continuously produced in extremely large numbers, but are dormant until puberty. Approximately once each month, generally from the fourteenth to the forty-fifth year, a follicle is singled out to become mature. A sac forms around the egg and fills with fluid and grows larger and larger until it bursts its wall on the surface of the ovary and the contained egg emerges from its follicle, leaves the ovary, and is picked up at the open end of a nearby tube (*Fallopian*). The egg is one of the largest body cells—primarily because it carries the food to nourish the embryo in its earliest stages if fertilization should occur.

Ovulation

The rupture of the follicle and the release of the egg is called ovulation. It is not usually triggered by sexual intercourse, but happens as a result of a complex relationship between the ovary and pituitary glands in a sequence of events called the menstrual cycle. This periodically equips a woman to produce an egg, to nest it if it is fertilized, and to nourish and harbor the new individual until birth.

Female Hormone

In addition to producing egg cells, ovaries are primarily responsible for the production of estrogen which in turn produces secondary sex characteristics like enlargement of the breasts, broadening and rounding of the hips, development of a fatty layer under the skin which makes a woman's body "soft" and "feminine," and growth of pubic hair. Female hormones are secreted internally into the blood stream. Although certain synthetic and natural hormone medications and creams can be given orally or applied locally with benefit, most of the "hormone" creams and potions promising rejuvenation will provide exercise and perhaps a psychological lift, but they will not transfer sufficient female hormones to the inside so that they can do any significant good.

If one ovary is defunct or removed the other usually produces sufficient hormones to maintain the secondary female characteristics, sexual desire, and the menstrual cycle. If surgical removal of both ovaries is necessary, the woman undergoes those changes associated with menopause.

Rotation of Egg Production

An egg may be produced by either ovary. It seems that the ovaries alternate; nevertheless women who have had one ovary removed can have a normal menstrual cycle, and one ovary *can* produce an egg each cycle. The incidence of two-egg twins and multiple births indicates that one ovary can produce more than one egg or that both ovaries can produce eggs in one cycle. Some women do not know when they ovulate; others may experience some symptom—a slight pain ("ovulation ping," or "mittelschmerz"), or a slight mucus discharge from the vagina.

Fallopian Tubes

How the egg gets from the ovary to the Fallopian tube is still only partially understood. The Fallopian tubes are each between

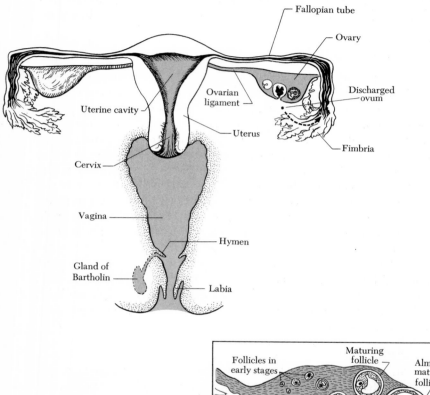

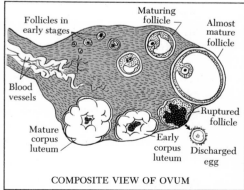

COMPOSITE VIEW OF OVUM

FIGURE 2.   *Female genital and reproductive organs (front view).*

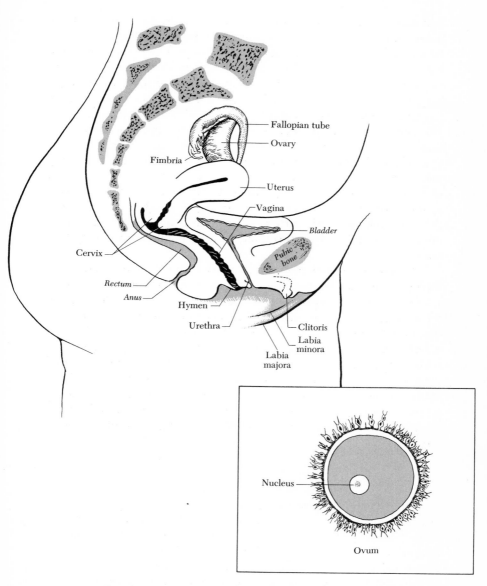

Female genital and reproductive organs (side view).

17

two and four inches long and partially encircle the ovaries. At the outer end of each tube there are petal-like projections (*fimbria*) which may aid in directing eggs into the tube. The outer wall of the tube is composed of muscle that contracts in a slow rhythmic manner and produces wavelike movements which are strongest near the time of ovulation. The cells lining the tubes have short hairlike structures (*cilia*) which create a current with their constant wavelike motion. Perhaps the egg is attracted to the tube by a combination of these factors, which then assist in transporting the egg through the Fallopian tube to the uterus. Since fertilization normally takes place in the outer third of the tube closest to the fimbriated end, the sperm cell accomplishing it has to have made its way against both forces. If fertilized, the egg cell takes three or four days to reach the uterus; otherwise it usually disintegrates. Its maximum susceptibility to fertilization is about eighteen to twenty-four hours.

In some rare cases the sperm may swim out the open end of the Fallopian tube and fertilize an egg in the ovary or abdominal cavity, which affixes itself to some other organ and begins to develop. In other cases a tube, partially blocked because of some inflammatory disease like gonorrhea, may permit the passage of a sperm but not a fertilized egg, and the egg may continue to develop in the tube without being able to travel to the uterus. At other times, impaired peristalsis of the tube will leave the developing egg stranded there. Such pregnancies (*ectopic*) usually terminate after the sixth or seventh week. In such cases, the developing embryo usually must be surgically removed, and the damage it has caused surgically repaired.

Female Sterilization

In a female sterilization operation the Fallopian tubes are tied off and cut—usually an irreversible process. It in no way affects sexual desire and gratification or other female functions such as menstruation, since the hormones produced by the ovaries are secreted directly into the blood stream. The operation is technically simple, but it does require an incision through the abdominal wall to reach the tubes and a recuperative period of four to five days.

Work is in progress on a simpler technique, which will apply metal or plastic clamps to the tubes via a small incision in the vagina.

Normally the fertilized egg makes its way through the Fallopian tube to the uterus, where it is implanted and nurtured until birth.

Uterus

The uterus is a most remarkable muscle. It is a firm, compact organ about the size and shape of a small pear, but it can grow and expand enough to hold a twenty-inch, nine-pound baby or more— and then within six weeks after the birth of the baby return to almost original size. It is normally so placed in the pelvis that the part corresponding to the stem end of the pear lies slightly below and behind the rest of the uterus. The upper part (*body*) connects with the Fallopian tubes. The rounded lower end (*cervix*) extends about a half-inch into the vagina, and its lining contains glands that provide a mucus fluid which attracts and stimulates sperm cells. Passing through the cervix is a small canal which connects the body of the uterus with the vaginal passage. Thus the Fallopian tubes, the body of the uterus, the cervical canal, and the vagina, provide a passage from the ovaries in the pelvic cavity to the outside of the body.

The lining of the uterus (*endometrium*) is especially prepared during the menstrual cycle to receive the fertilized egg. Some linings do not do this job well, and because of this or any of a large number of other factors, the fertilized egg may be aborted. Preventive hormone therapy has, however, decreased the risk. When an egg is defective or implantation is poor, the slightest physical upset may detach it, particularly at times when the menstrual flow would have occurred if pregnancy had not supervened. On the other hand, once a healthy egg firmly implants itself in the endometrium, it is generally sustained through pregnancy to birth.

For a variety of reasons, removal of the uterus (*hysterectomy*) may become necessary. This, of course, precludes the possibility of conception, but the conservative surgery now commonly performed insures the ability to have and enjoy sex relations. The vagina is suitably reformed, and the ovaries (unless diseased) are left intact to continue their production of female hormones, allowing the functions which these hormones sustain to continue.

Menstrual Cycle

If fertilization does not occur, the especially prepared and thickened lining of the uterus is no longer needed and superficial layers are shed as the menstrual flow. Menstruation is a normal physiological process which signals the coming of puberty.

The pituitary, a small gland the size of a pea located at the base of the brain, largely controls the menstrual cycle in combination with the ovaries. Its two secretory areas are called the anterior and posterior lobes. The secretion of the anterior lobe, however, exerts the greatest influence on the ovaries, and through them, on the menstrual cycle. During a girl's early life this anterior lobe regulates general bodily growth, but at puberty its activity becomes greatly increased and in a period of a few months she usually acquires full powers of reproduction. A lag of a few months to several years has been noted by some authorities between the onset of the menstrual cycle and the ability of some young girls to conceive. Its cause is unknown.

The interaction of hormones from the ovaries and pituitary gland is complex. The development of any particular follicle (the sac in which the egg is contained) is influenced by the follicle stimulating hormone (FSH) from the anterior lobe of the pituitary gland. As the follicle itself matures, it in turn secretes the follicular hormone (FH) which stimulates the growth and development of the endometrium in preparation for the reception of the fertilized egg.

After ovulation (when the egg has left the follicle), another hormone in the anterior pituitary, the luteinizing hormone (LH), causes the development of the corpus luteum from the lining of the ruptured follicle at its site.

The corpus luteum in turn produces the hormones estrogen and progesterone which help to prepare the endometrium for implantation and nourishment of the egg. At the same time, it secretes increasing amounts of the follicular hormone, which gradually causes a reduction in the pituitary gland's production of the hormone maintaining the corpus luteum, which then gradually shrinks. In turn, the hormone-producing capacity of the corpus luteum

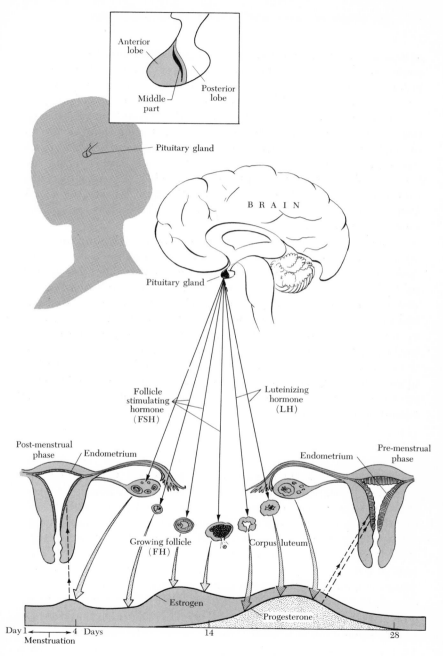

Anterior
lobe

Posterior
lobe

Middle
part

Pituitary gland

B R A I N

Pituitary gland

Follicle
stimulating
hormone
(FSH)

Luteinizing
hormone
(LH)

Post-menstrual
phase

Endometrium

Endometrium

Pre-menstrual
phase

Growing follicle
(FH)

Corpus luteum

Estrogen

Progesterone

Day 1 ← → 4 Days
Menstruation

14

28

FIGURE 3.   *Hormonal regulation of the menstrual cycle.*

ceases, the premenstrual lining disintegrates as a result of the hormone withdrawal, and the menstrual flow begins. The anterior pituitary is again free to produce the follicle-stimulating hormone, a new follicle starts to develop, and another menstrual cycle begins.

Menstruation usually starts between the eleventh and thirteenth years, but occasionally it appears as early as the ninth or as late as the eighteenth. Interestingly enough the earlier a girl starts to menstruate, the longer her reproductive span usually lasts. During the first year of the menstrual cycle, a girl may have irregular periods, even skipping a month or so. It may take time for her body and glands to adjust to the cycle, but by the end of the first year periods usually come regularly.

The menstrual cycle is a continuous process covering an average of twenty-eight days. There is no specific time span for this cycle. For some women it may last twenty-one days, for others thirty-five or more. So long as the woman's cycle remains regular and constant, there is no apparent relation between these variations and either health or fertility. However, all other things being equal, a woman with a twenty-eight-day cycle has a slightly greater chance for becoming pregnant than a woman with a thirty-five-day cycle; the former ovulates thirteen times a year to the latter's ten. For this discussion let us arbitrarily select a cycle of twenty-eight days, which begins with the first day of the menstrual flow. The cycle is composed of four phases:

Menstrual Phase

Conception did not occur in the previous cycle and the endometrium has started to shed as the menstrual flow. About two ounces of blood, thin watery fluid, and tissue are discarded following nonfertilization of an egg. Menstruation itself is of variable duration, from woman to woman, lasting from one to eight days, though the average is three to five. Deviations are entirely compatible with good health, but if a woman notices a marked change from her own normal pattern she should see a physician. Usually menstruation is not accompanied by any marked discomfort. Ordinarily only a sense of weight is present in the pelvis (or some mild cramps or backache), and perhaps some nervousness and lassitude. It cannot be repeated too often that menstruation is not a sickness. Ill health may affect it but normal menstruation is an evidence of good health. The menstrual phase lasts about four days.

 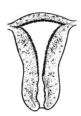 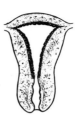 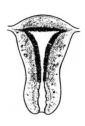

Menstrual phase   Postmenstrual phase   Intermenstrual phase   Premenstrual phase

FIGURE 4.   *Phases of the menstrual cycle.*

Postmenstrual Phase

Immediately after menstruation the endometrium is thin. On about the third or fourth day after the onset of menstruation the pituitary sends out hormones (FSH) to the ovaries, and one egg begins to ripen. The endometrium is dormant. This resting stage lasts approximately five days, which takes us to day nine in the cycle.

Intermenstrual Phase

The ovaries now release a special hormone (FH) to the endometrium, which begins to thicken. About the fifth day of this phase (and the fourteenth day in the cycle), a mature egg breaks out of its follicle. Ovulation has taken place. The egg then enters one of the Fallopian tubes. If the egg is fertilized in the tube, it will travel to the uterus and the endometrium will provide a nesting place for its development. This phase lasts fourteen days, and we reach day twenty-three in the cycle.

Premenstrual Phase

The endometrium is thick, ready for the egg. If the egg is fertilized, it remains imbedded in this well-nourished tissue. Pregnancy continues, and there is no menstruation. The menstrual cycle begins again about five to eight weeks after the child is born, unless the mother nurses the child beyond that period. (Nursing—lactation—

usually suppresses ovulation.) If the egg is not fertilized, it disintegrates and is absorbed; and since the thickened uterine lining is no longer needed, the upper layers begin to shed. The deeper portion is retained for regrowth.

The premenstrual phase lasts about five days—completing the cycle of twenty-eight days.

Despite the fact that menstruation is a normal and desirable physiological process, some women fear it or suffer from it in part because of the superstitions and misconceptions still surrounding it. Age-old taboos, rooted in misinformation and fear, are very much in evidence when individuals avoid the very word *menstruation* with damning phrases like "the curse" and still believe that a menstruating woman will wilt flowers if she touches them. In ancient Persia, a menstruating woman was thought to be possessed of an evil spirit. In ancient Rome, she was blamed for blighting crops. In Moslem and Mosaic laws she was considered unclean and had to live in separate quarters during the period. It was even believed by some that menstrual flow and urine came from the same part of the body—another reason for the association with uncleanliness. It is understandable that people, primitive and contemporary alike, without knowledge of the physiology of menstruation, would create fantasies about it. A knowledge of the facts should eliminate fear and confusion.

However, improved knowledge of the menstrual process is not enough by itself to remove fear. Women may view the impending menstrual flow with trepidation for a variety of reasons. For the woman wishing to conceive, it will be a sign of another failure. She may feel depressed and weep in frustration at her inability. For the woman who does not wish a child the prospect of the "missed period" may be worrisome. Even to a woman who wants a child the thought of pregnancy may be frightening. Until recently pregnancy was a real threat to a woman's life. Trained obstetricians, antibiotics, blood banks, modern hospitals, modern surgery have markedly reduced the dangers, but they are still vivid in the minds of some women.

For most women, there is no biological reason for considerable discomfort during menstruation, but there is for some. The uterus becomes engorged with dilated blood vessels during this period, and if it is tipped so that the menstrual flow cannot easily get through the cervical canal, or if there is a tight cervical muscle, discomfort might well result. The woman in a generally poor physical condition may find the congested pelvic organs unusually burdensome, and other symptoms of menstruation may further debilitate her already weak organs and systems. But severe and prolonged menstrual cramps, nausea, vomiting, and other marked symptoms should be investigated. And, of course, while normal menstrual functioning is closely related to good physical health, the mental set of the woman can be important. Her positive attitude toward menstruation (perhaps largely taken from that of her mother), and her acceptance of her role as a woman with creative reproductive powers of which the menstrual cycle is a physical manifestation, help to offset whatever discomfort there might be.

On the other hand, there is sometimes a tendency to feel "blue" when a period is about to start and this condition is called menstrual tension. The hormones that stimulate the endometrium to thicken, also stimulate a feeling of well-being. Just before menstruation, these hormones recede and a let-down feeling may follow briefly. Part of this heavy, depressed, uncomfortable feeling is due to the fluids in the system at this time. Women feel "puffy" and heavy. They may find it difficult to live with themselves. They are unsure of themselves and may need extra understanding.

The most common methods for menstrual hygiene are disposable napkins kept in place externally by a belt and tampons that in most cases can be inserted into the vagina without disturbing the hymen. These new methods minimize the malaise and sense of messiness. With them it is possible for a menstruating woman to do just about anything she is used to. Horseback riding, skating, dancing are all possible, and with tampons so is swimming on the "tapering off" days. She feels freer and less restricted by her "sick" days and less conscious of whether others (particularly males) know she is menstruating.

Menopause

The menstrual cycle usually ceases in the mid-to-late forties. The cessation of follicle growth in most women is gradual and is manifested by greater irregularity and increasingly long intervals between menstrual periods. After years of work the ovaries complete their ovulatory function, but still perform other functions, such as the internal secretion of the female hormone. This is one reason why modern medical practice is careful to preserve the ovaries during pelvic surgery.

The time of reproductive decline is known as the climacteric, menopause, or "change of life." Occasionally a woman will erroneously believe she is no longer producing egg cells and will give up contraceptive precautions. Conception in such situations is not uncommon and the resulting children have come to be known as "change of life" babies. At least two years without a menstrual period should go by before a woman can feel fairly certain that she is not going to ovulate again.

At menopause the hormonal pattern controlling the menstrual cycle is disrupted, and until an adjustment is made, the entire glandular system may be thrown slightly off balance. In sympathetic response the nervous system may also be affected, and a woman will experience anxiety, hot flushes, sweating, palpitations of the heart, headaches, and top of the head pressures which make them feel as if they are "blowing their lids." Some women also go through stages of depression, irritability, easy crying, oversensitiveness, making scenes. For some, the end of childbearing means the end of femininity, the end of being sexually attractive, worthwhile human beings. The girl who has marked menstrual depressions is frequently the woman who has depressions at menopause. But often this person will not suffer from menstrual depression during the childbearing and childrearing years.

A girl develops her femininity in large part by the acceptance of not having a penis and makes up for this by looking forward to bearing a child. Much of this is unconscious. (See the genital phase of psychosexual development in Chapter Three.) In puberty she is given all outer manifestations of womanhood and femininity: menstrual cycle and secondary sexual attributes like breasts and rounded hips. She blooms forth into her full beauty as a woman. At menopause, she realizes that she will no longer be able to perform her ultimate feminine goal of childbearing, and that from then on her looks and attractiveness will decline. Depression may be particularly severe if having children has been a significant part of the woman's life, and she can find no satisfactory substitute when it is gone.

A woman's difficulty at menopause is proportionate to her general emotional health. If she has been fairly stable most of her life she stands a good chance of taking the menopause in her stride. In fact, most women seem undisturbed by these physical and psychological influences and their menopausal adjustment is relatively smooth and easy. For them, other glands, like the adrenal, come to the rescue, secreting modest amounts of hormones akin to those of the retiring ovaries until stabilization is reached. But, if nature does not adequately take over, hormone therapy can be helpful.

Some of a woman's anxiety over menopause is because of a deep fear that this change will reduce her desire for or pleasure in sex relations; fortunately, this is usually not the case and the opposite may well be true. Removal of fear of pregnancy permits her to relax more in intercourse, with greater emotional release. In fact, her mate may find it difficult to keep up with her new sexual demands, if his own are declining.

The impact of menopause is so varied and complex that it is not understood or tolerated very well by either sex. Women who have a relatively symptom-free menopause feel that women who are markedly disturbed either physically or emotionally are "weak sisters" looking for attention and sympathy and pampering themselves unduly.

Husbands and children are sometimes confused and irritated by a woman's menopausal symptoms. The tensions of the family relationship become more noticeable. Men sometimes may go through their own hormonal withdrawal symptoms (usually milder than those of women) in their late fifties and they can then appreciate better what their wives experienced ten or so years before.

female accessory organs

Labia

Omitted from the discussion thus far are the female organs which, while accessories to the sexual act, do not figure directly in reproduction. Outermost of these organs are rounded folds of skin and fatty tissue (*labia majora*) or outer lips which are covered by pubic hair and which protect the structures lying between them and the vagina. Just inside the labia majora are two smaller and thinner folds (*labia minora*), or inner lips. Both sets, but especially the inner lips, are liberally supplied with nerve endings, and upon stimulation become slightly engorged, increasing the female's desire for intercourse.

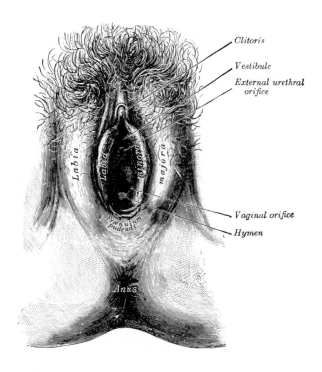

FIGURE 5.   *Female accessory organs.*

Hymen

Just inside the entrance to the vagina and partially closing the vaginal inlet is a membrane known as the hymen. This membrane has one or more perforations through which the menstrual flow leaves the body. In some women this opening is small, and the hymen forms almost a complete membrane; in others it may be only a thin rim of soft tissue around the entrance to the vagina. If a tampon menstrual guard is used, it can be inserted through the opening. There are women, however, who have so small an opening in the hymen that insertion of a tampon is painful. They can use some other type of menstrual guard, until the opening is enlarged.

The hymen has a biological purpose which seems to be limited to young children. Before puberty an intact hymen keeps out of the vagina some of the microorganisms causing infection, and minimizes the insertion of fingers and the usual foreign material that children seem to want to insert in any and all body openings. After puberty, secretions of the vagina guard it against most infection.

In the adult female the hymen serves no biological function except as a highly sensitive organ responsive to sexual stimulation. Nevertheless cultural and sexual significance is often associated with it. The intact hymen (*maidenhead*) is regarded as a symbol of virginity; and if a virgin is prized, it is deemed the husband's privilege and responsibility to rupture the hymen by the initial intercourse after marriage. The slight bleeding resulting from stretching or tearing is considered the ultimate test of a woman's virginity. In fact, however, the hymen can be stretched or dilated in many ways previous to the first intercourse so that blood does not necessarily accompany that act. The stretching, dilation, or tearing of the hymen can be painful and uncomfortable. But if the couple show love and consideration to each other, the act should ordinarily be a pleasant rather than a painful experience. It is not unusual, however, for several attempts to be made before full penetration is achieved.

It should be understood that women can participate in forms of sexual experience which might be thought undesirable by the prospective husband but which will, for all that, leave the hymen intact. If the virginity of one or both parties to a prospective marriage is an important question, then they owe it to each other to ask it. If proof beyond the answer is thought necessary, then it would be wise to ponder the desirability of going ahead with a marriage already endangered by doubt, mistrust, and suspicion.

Urethra

Forward of the vaginal opening, and within the inner lips, is the opening of the urethra, the canal that connects the bladder with the outside of the body and through which urine is excreted. The urethra is separate from the sex organs and does not relate in any way to reproduction or sex foreplay, except that the external opening is sensitive to stimulation.

Clitoris

Where the upper folds of the inner lips converge is a structure which resembles a very small penis (clitoris). It is plentifully supplied with nerves and blood vessels, becomes engorged, and enlarges and throbs under sexual excitement. It is a major source of pleasure in sexual intercourse. Since it is probably the most sensitive of the female sex organs, girls and women sometimes agitate it with their hands or with thigh pressure to gain sexual gratification. In female masturbation it is the organ most frequently used to bring on a climax, particularly by the young girl who does not wish to disturb her hymen by inserting things into her vagina or manipulating it.

Because the clitoris is so sensitive, and is sometimes the instrument of orgasm, a man preparing a woman for sexual intercourse may stimulate it by gentle massage. This and similar preparatory techniques—kissing, breastplay, caressing and fondling—are called sex foreplay. The newly married woman may be accustomed to deriving pleasure and even climax from clitoral manipulation, but not from insertion of the penis into the vagina. When full response, or orgasm, to the insertion and action of the penis is achieved, it may be found to be the more strongly pleasurable and more deeply satisfying of the two. The husband, however, may have to stimulate the clitoris considerably with his penis or hands before and during intercourse to assist his wife with the transition.

Female Orgasm

There is some question whether the female experiences two distinct types of orgasm. A woman usually reaches orgasm either by stimulation of the clitoris, or by vaginal penetration, or by some combination of both. Orgasm when reached, however, is a complex response difficult to ascribe to a single cause. At least the physiological response in orgasm for women seems to be the same no matter how the orgasm is precipitated. But women often note a qualitative difference between clitoral and vaginal orgasm, and express a distinct preference for the latter.

The female orgasm is not so well understood as that of the male. When a man reaches orgasm, he has an ejaculation accompanied by muscle spasm, and this happens at the climax, when strong and general muscular movements culminate in powerful pelvic thrusts accompanying ejaculation. His response, though somewhat general and diffuse, is largely limited to the genital area.

Less is known about the female orgasm. The female has a less obvious focal point for sexual stimulation and gratification. Women seem to be more emotionally involved than men in their sexual experiences, and are therefore more reluctant to talk about them. Though some of a man's sexual needs are emotionally derived, he also needs the relief from physical tension and discomfort in the sex organs that is accomplished by ejaculation. A woman's need, however, is predominantly of an emotional, erotic nature. This does not mean that a woman's need is less; it simply has different sources. This implies that male and female orgasms are diffierent.

Women who have experienced an orgasm are able to describe it in physical terms only about as well as men could were there no ejaculation to describe. The female orgasm produces contractions around the rim of the vagina with perhaps some spasm of the muscles of the vagina. The uterus tilts slightly upwards. There is a general release of bodily and genital and emotional tension; she feels the need to show tenderness and warmth to her partner. It may come soon after the man's ejaculation, and it subsides more slowly than that of the man. She has a feeling of lassitude for some time afterward. Whether a woman is able to have an orgasm depends more on her psychological makeup and her acceptance of her feminine role in life than on the skill of the male partner as a lover.

Breasts

The breasts of both sexes are erogenous zones, but especially the fully developed breast tissue of the woman. The breasts (*mammary glands*) are present in both sexes at birth, but only those of the woman develop fully to equip her for her function of suckling infants. The weight and dimensions of the breasts differ from woman to woman, and at different periods in the same woman's life. Before puberty the breasts are small. At puberty, the increased estrogen in the system elongates the mammary ducts; this along with the growth of the breast tissue shows in increasing size and

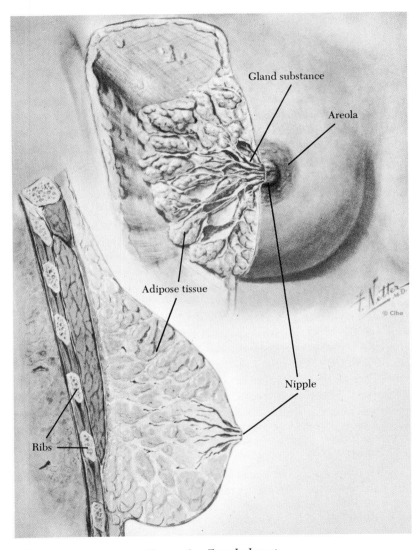

Gland substance

Areola

Adipose tissue

Nipple

Ribs

FIGURE 6. *Female breast.*

32

firmness of the breasts as they are made ready to function in lactation. The breasts increase markedly in size during pregnancy and
lactation; they atrophy in old age. The left breast is generally a
little larger than the right.

In the fully developed woman, the breasts are dome shaped,
soft to the touch, and have at the center an area called the areola,
the surface of which appears rough because of the sebacious glands
just under it. The secretion of these glands lubricates the nipple
which is in the center of the areola. The smooth muscles of the
areola stiffen the nipple for better grasp by the suckling infant. The
nipple also becomes erect from stimulation like sexual foreplay. The
nipple is the outlet for fifteen to twenty tiny ducts which carry and
store the milk from the mammary glands.

At puberty the areola and nipple grow and become pigmented.
In the unmarried, nonpregnant woman the areola has a pinkish hue;
about two months after conception, it enlarges and acquires a darker
tinge which grows even darker as the pregnancy progresses. The
color becomes lighter at the termination of pregnancy and lactation,
but it always remains darker than it was originally. Only during
pregnancy do those changes occur which make milk production possible. Lactation starts three to four days after delivery; once initi-
ated it is stimulated and maintained through the act of sucking.

The breasts may also be a source of anxiety. Those who have
not fully accepted their feminine role, consciously or unconsciously,
do not want them, and may be embarrassed or ashamed of them as
symbols of femininity. If the breasts are or are imagined to be
overdeveloped or underdeveloped, there may be severe psychic
consequences. Difficulty may also arise over what is considered
ideal for different ethnic and social groups and at different historical periods.

Glands of Bartholin

Although a woman does not ejaculate during the sex act, she
does lubricate, and the extent of this is directly related to her readiness for the sex act. Several glands contribute to lubrication, but the
Glands of Bartholin are among the most important. Situated at each
side of the entrance to the vagina, they secrete a fluid which mois-
tens and lubricates the tissues surrounding the opening of the vagina. This lubricant, which can be detected with the fingers, in-

dicates readiness for intercourse. If the act takes place before lubrication, penetration is difficult, uncomfortable, and less pleasurable for both persons. When women do not lubricate sufficiently (not uncommon after menopause), artificial lubricants are sometimes introduced, particularly when a condom is also used. But these lubricants should not substitute for foreplay to produce natural lubrication.

Vagina

Extending back from the inner lips to the cervix of the uterus and slightly beyond is a thin-walled elastic cavity (vagina). At rest this cavity is closed, with the walls touching each other. They are separated by the menstrual flow, intercourse, childbirth, and when they are mechanically parted as with a tampon menstrual guard or a douche. It is at the cervical end of this cavity that the sperm cells are deposited during sexual intercourse. The vagina is about four inches long but can be considerably distended in length and width. It is the birth canal capable of permitting passage of a fully-developed fetus and usually of accommodating an erect penis over six inches long.

fertilization

During intercourse, the semen (containing the sperm cells) is deposited at the cervical end of the vagina, and some of the sperm cells make their way into the cervical mucus and through the cervical canal. By a whiplash motion of their tails, at a rate of about an inch in eight minutes, they move toward the cervical opening of the uterus. The environment there is more favorable than in the vagina, where they can survive and retain their motility for only a few hours at the most. They then swim through the mucus of the cervix and uterine canal to the Fallopian tubes, where in spite of prevailing currents and peristaltic action against them, they find an even more favorable and nourishing environment. This phenomenon of seeking a favorable environment (tropism) is a strong force in nature. The movements of roots toward water and leaves toward sun are other examples. Sperm cells go into both Fallopian tubes, not only the one in which an egg might be located. If one

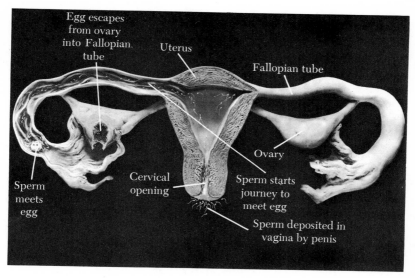

Egg escapes
from ovary
into Fallopian
tube

Uterus

Fallopian tube

Ovary

Sperm
meets
egg

Cervical
opening

Sperm starts
journey to
meet egg

Sperm deposited in
vagina by penis

FIGURE 7.   *Fertilization.*

penetrates the egg, a rapid change takes place in the membrane of
the egg so that others are turned away. The competition is great,
and usually only the best equipped sperm accomplishes penetration.
Only the head and neck of the sperm penetrate the egg. The less
the intrusion of foreign matter into the egg, the better for the development of the new individual. When penetration occurs, the twenty-
three chromosomes of the sperm unite with the twenty-three of the
egg to form a nucleus (*zygote*) of a new cell with a full complement
of twenty-three pairs. The new cell soon begins to undergo typical
(*mitotic*) cell division. It slowly passes through the Fallopian tube
and comes to rest on the nourishing membrane lining of the uterus,
where it begins to sink its roots into the site of implantation.

pregnancy and childbirth

PREGNANCY BEGINS at conception, and under normal conditions is climaxed by the delivery of a child approximately nine months later. This period terminates about six weeks after delivery when the mother's organs have adapted to the demands of the child and have recovered their regular size and function. Pregnancy will be discussed in three stages: conception to labor (prenatal), labor and delivery, adaptation and recovery (postnatal). At the same time we will relate each stage to the corresponding external bodily changes and emotional symptoms a mother experiences.

conception to labor

During intercourse the penis elongates the vaginal canal into a tubelike structure with the cervix of the uterus at the upper end. The male ejaculate is thrown onto the mucus that surrounds the cervix and covers the cervical opening. Most of the sperm cells in the ejaculate are concentrated in the first few drops that adhere tenaciously to the mucus—one reason why douching as a contraceptive is not reliable. The alkaline ejaculate acts as a buffer to neutralize the acid vaginal secretion, which otherwise would immobilize the sperm in a short time. Most of the sperm does remain in the vagina and dies within a few hours.

The healthy and active sperm cells deposited on the cervical mucus work their way through the cervical canal and uterus to the Fallopian tubes, the usual site for fertilization. They go into both tubes, not only the one in which an egg might be present. The journey is only five to seven inches, but it may take eight minutes to eight hours or longer. Sperm cells do not travel in a straight line, and they must swim against the downward and outward currents of the uterus and Fallopian tubes. These currents are created by cilia on the cells lining the tubes, by peristalsis of the tubes, and by mild rhythmic contractions of the uterus. The migration is rigorous, usually leaving behind weak and abnormal sperm.

When discharged from the ovary the egg is surrounded by a protective and nourishing layer of cells. These are thought to be softened by the impact of many sperm before one can reach the egg membrane. But even then a number of sperm approach the membrane, try to penetrate, make a dent, and are tossed back. Certain areas of the membrane may be more resistant than others.

As soon as the head and neck of one sperm cell penetrates the egg, the membrane becomes impenetrable to any other. The nucleus in the head and the centrosome in the neck are necessary to start the fertilization process. The tail, no longer necessary, disintegrates. The other sperm, having played their part, live for a few hours in the invigorating environment of the tubes and then also disintegrate.

Soon after penetration, the twenty-three chromosomes of the sperm unite with the twenty-three of the egg to form the nucleus (*zygote*) of a new cell. The twenty-three new pairs of chromosomes (a total of forty-six) comprise the total biological heritage of the new individual. Ultimately, this initial cell grows into a fully developed child—one cell becomes two, two become four, and so on into the billions. The material to make the cells comes initially from the egg itself, and then from nutrients supplied by the mother.

The cells begin specializing very early. Each chromosome is composed of from tens to hundreds of genes that act like catalysts in directing the development of every part of the body. Some cells give rise to muscle, some to skin, blood, brain, bone; others form the organs essential to the safe development of the child within the mother.

The fertilized egg undergoes cell division as it travels down the Fallopian tube. After three to four days it reaches the uterus and comes to rest in the folds in the lining of the uterine wall. The lining meanwhile has thickened and increased its blood and nutrient supply to nourish and support this little cluster of cells (*blastocyst*), which burrows into the membrane of the uterine wall. Then begins the differentiation of the cells into the organs of the developing individual, and into the various structures that will contain him until birth.

Egg

The period of the egg, or blastocyst, lasts about two weeks, beginning with fertilization and ending with implantation of the blastocyst in the uterine lining. There is much cell division during this period, but it is accomplished with little increase in size (the

FIGURE 8.   *Implantation.*

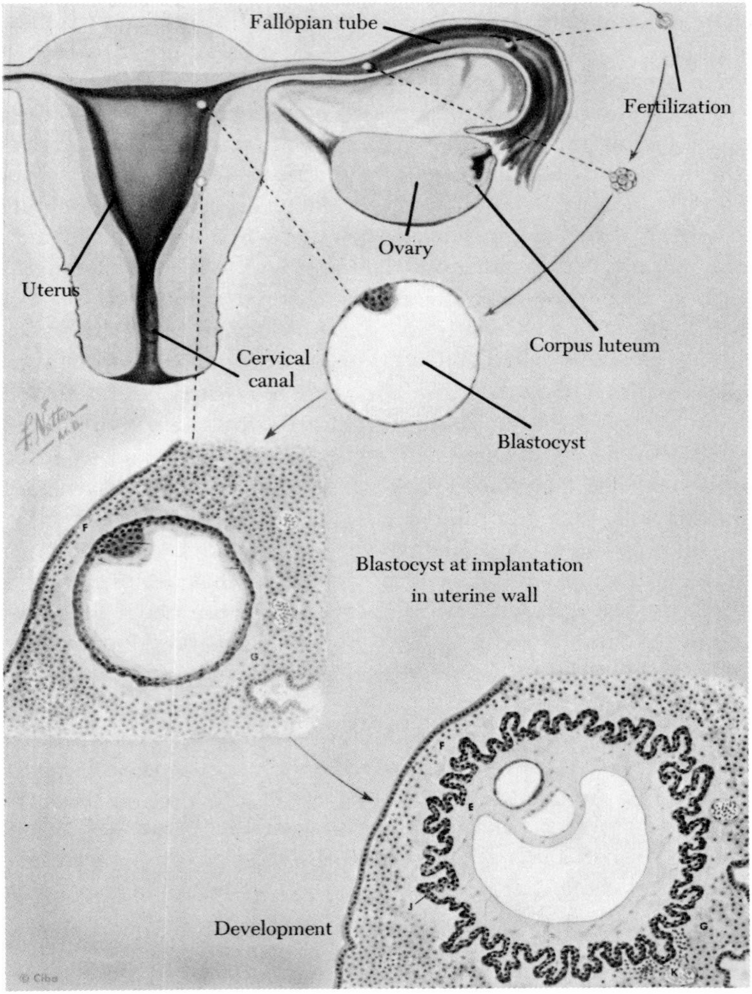

Fallopian tube

Fertilization

Ovary

Uterus

Corpus luteum

Cervical canal

Blastocyst

Blastocyst at implantation in uterine wall

Development

blastocyst measures a sixteenth of an inch) since an appreciable amount of growth cannot take place until nourishment from maternal circulation is available. Various organs begin to form: the embryonic disc from which the embryo and infant will develop, the amniotic sac in which the developing individual is housed and protected, and the yolk sac from which he receives preliminary feeding. However, there are not yet any outward signs of pregnancy.

Embryo

For the next six weeks the individual is called an embryo. During this time almost all his cells are differentiated and all organs formed. By the end of the period, the human character of the embryo can easily be recognized.

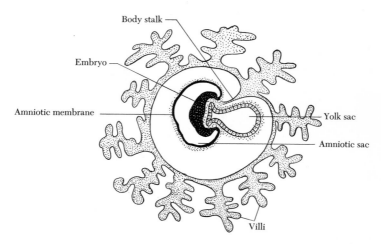

FIGURE 9.   *Early embryonic development.*

The beginning of this period is marked by the refinement of organs connecting mother and child. Branching structures (*villi*) arise from the wall of the blastocyst and hold the embryo in place in the uterine lining. Through the villi, nutrition from the maternal circulating blood reaches the embryo, and in turn, wastes from the embryo pass into the maternal blood.

The mother's blood is rich in food materials and oxygen, both essential to the embryo. By a transfer process (*osmosis*) that permits certain substances to pass through a membrane, nutrient ma-

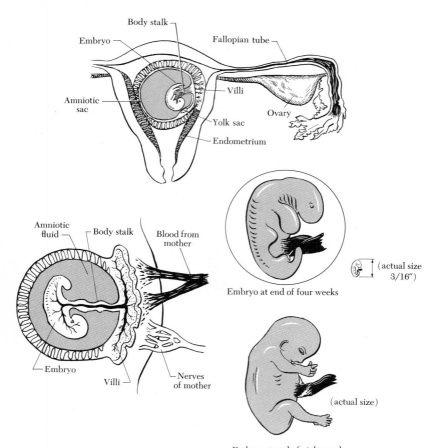

Body stalk

Embryo

Fallopian tube

Amniotic sac

Villi

Yolk sac

Ovary

Endometrium

Amniotic fluid

Body stalk

Blood from mother

Embryo

Villi

Nerves of mother

Embryo at end of four weeks

(actual size 3/16″)

(actual size)

Embryo at end of eight weeks

FIGURE 10. *Late embryonic development.*

terials and oxygen leave the maternal blood, pass through the walls of the villi and enter the blood circulating in the vessels within the villi. This blood goes through the body stalk bringing the necessary nutrients to the embryo.

The waste products of the embryo are removed by a reversal of the process. As the blood from the embryo flows through the body stalk to the villi, carbon dioxide and other wastes pass into the maternal blood. From there they are carried by the mother's circulating blood to her lungs and kidneys and excreted along with her own waste products. All exchanges of food and waste between the mother and embryo are carried out in this way. There is no direct intermixture of blood.

The embryo is much smaller and more highly developed than is commonly known. At the end of the fifth week it is little more than a third of an inch long, yet in rudimentary form it has nearly all the structures and organs that the infant will eventually have. At the end of the eighth week, the termination of the embryonic period, it weighs less than one-fifteenth of an ounce and is about one and one-half inches long. In spite of its small size, however, its impact on the system of the mother yields some definite and discernible signs and symptoms of pregnancy.

Signs of Pregnancy

Women who suspect pregnancy want to know for sure as soon as possible. The most obvious early sign is a missed menstrual period. Of course, there may be other reasons for a missed or delayed period—physiological (e.g., thyroid imbalance, anemia), emotional or organic. Before going to a physician for examination women usually wait for a week or two after the period should normally have occurred. The physician applies certain criteria, any one or a number of which may determine whether a woman is pregnant.

One sign is increased fullness of the breasts. Most women feel a heaviness and fullness of the breasts preceding menstruation. If they are pregnant, the fullness continues beyond the time when menstruation would usually occur. The congestion produces a slight secretion which can be expressed by gentle pressure on the nipple about two or three weeks after the period has been missed. At about the same time the pigmentation at the base of the nipples darkens, followed by a darkening of the nipples themselves. Pigmentation might also show up later in other body areas such as the face and the mid-line of the lower abdominal wall. The cause of pigmentation in these areas is unknown.

A portion of the bladder is attached to the uterus, and any distension, congestion, or development of the uterus affects the bladder, causing another sign—frequent urination from mild irritation.

An examination of the reproductive organs reveals other signs. The cervix of the uterus takes on a slightly bluish tint, as does the vaginal membrane, and becomes softer. The uterus itself becomes somewhat larger and softer and the lower segment just above the cervix thins out. Sometimes, by internal pelvic examination, it is possible to feel the ovary from which the fertilized egg came; in pregnancy that ovary will feel somewhat larger than the other one.

One of the classic early symptoms of pregnancy—though by no means a positive indication—is a tendency to nausea and vomiting ("morning sickness"). Ordinarily, it begins about two or three weeks after the menstrual period has been missed. This is not so common a symptom as is generally thought. It is experienced to a marked degree by only 40 to 50 per cent of pregnant women. However, many more experience mild nausea. While the cause of "morning sickness" is unknown, it can be readily controlled with oral medication. Like other symptoms it is not by itself a positive indication of pregnancy.

One more sign, particularly useful to the childless woman who wishes to conceive, is a sustained elevated basal body temperature. The woman takes her body temperature in the morning before getting out of bed. The temperature of the normally ovulating woman is lower in the first half of her cycle, and somewhat higher (about one-half degree) following ovulation. If her menstrual period is missed and her temperature stays up through and beyond the time her period was due, this is a presumptive sign of pregnancy.

One of the most reliable indications of pregnancy is the result of the A-Z (Ascheim-Zondek) test or one similar to it. These tests are based on the fact that the developing embryo secretes gonad-stimulating hormones that appear in the pregnant woman's blood and urine. If a small amount of the pregnant woman's urine or blood serum containing this hormone is injected into a female mouse or rabbit that has not yet undergone its first spontaneous ovulation, the ovaries of the animal will mature rapidly and form eggs, an easily recognized change. With this test, pregnancy in a woman can usually be determined within ten days after a missed period. Positive results are 97 per cent reliable when the test is properly performed. However, if the test is given shortly after the menstrual period is missed, and the result is negative, the possibility of pregnancy should not be ruled out entirely. It may yield positive results a week or ten days later when the concentration of hormones in the woman's urine or blood serum are increased.

There are now also hormonal oral tests for pregnancy. For four days, a woman takes progesterone tablets, the withdrawal of which will induce the menstrual flow if she is not pregnant. This test is simple, but evidence of its reliability has not been convincing thus far.

With the exception of the A-Z test, each of the signs discussed is in and of itself simply a presumption of pregnancy; however, by the second or third week after missing a menstrual period, it has usually been possible to gather enough evidence to let a woman know definitely whether or not she is pregnant.

Recently several simple tests have been developed which are based on the presence of human chorionic gonadotropin (HCG) in the body fluids and urine of the pregnant woman. The tests can be done in the physician's office and do not require laboratory animals. A drop of urine is added to specifically prepared agents. If the woman supplying the urine is not pregnant, agglutination occurs; if she is pregnant, there is no agglutination. Depending on the test used, the determination can be made in from four to fourteen days after a missed menstrual period, with results available in from three minutes to two hours. The reliability of the test is as high as 96 per cent depending on the time elapsed between the missed menstrual period and the administration of the test.

Visit With Obstetrician

The obstetrician, familiar with the problems of pregnancy and how to deal with them, should be consulted as soon as pregnancy has been determined. He helps the woman to understand what is going on within her body, the influence her condition and actions have on the development of the child, and the need to make this influence as positive as possible. Obviously she wishes to find someone whose medical competence she trusts but also someone to whom she can talk freely, and who will "understand" her. The first visit gives her and the obstetrician a chance to create the foundation of a strong relationship that will continue throughout the pregnancy.

The obstetrician immediately makes clear to his patient that pregnancy is a healthy, normal physiological function of the female body, not an illness, and that he is going to keep her as well equipped as possible to fulfill her function. He is interested in her menstrual history as an influence on the conduct of the pregnancy—age of onset, regularity, number of days of flow, amount of flow, and pain. He calculates with her the approximate date of delivery—by adding seven days to the first day of the last normal menstrual period, and counting back three months. (Thus if the first day of the last menstrual period is March 1, the baby is due next December 8.) If previous pregnancies ended in childbirth, he asks about the character, duration, discomfort, and aftereffects of labor and delivery.

Medical Examination

A complete medical history is taken to help evaluate a patient's capacity to stand the stresses and strains of pregnancy and labor. This is followed by a complete physical examination (especially heart, kidneys, and lungs) providing a record of a woman's present condition to compare with her condition during the course of the pregnancy. The physician may suggest means for correcting any possible toxic factors (e.g., infected teeth, sinuses) and takes measures to improve the patient's general health during the pregnancy, for her sake as well as the child's.

The physical examination includes a thorough pelvic examination—vagina, cervix, position, size, and normalcy of uterus. The obstetrician warns against douches except on his specific advice for vaginal discharges and infections, because these may irritate the cervix and disturb the pregnancy. He evaluates the internal and external structure of the pelvis to determine the size and shape of the woman's bony structure in relation to the anticipated delivery of the child. If her pelvic structure seems normal, she is told so and assured that in all probability she can expect a normal delivery. The obstetrician then customarily asks questions and provides information about matters that should be understood as early as possible in the pregnancy.

Weight Control and Diet

The patient is instructed in weight control and diet. She is usually advised to limit the gain during pregnancy to between fifteen and twenty pounds, spaced if possible to less than two pounds a month. It is unpleasant—and sad—to see a trim, well built young woman destroy her physique by gaining too much weight during pregnancy. She may think she will lose it after the baby comes, but, on the average, a woman will lose only about fifteen pounds after the birth of her baby, including the weight of the baby itself, the "bag of waters," the placenta and related organs, and the gradual shrinking of the uterus and other pelvic organs.

Weight control also minimizes the chances of complications during pregnancy. The additional load that the needs of the developing child place on the mother's kidneys, heart, liver, and circulation in general might be dangerously increased by the added burden placed on these same organs by sudden and excessive weight gain.

After proper instruction most women make a valiant effort to limit weight gain. Sometimes a woman fails because of an emotional hunger she is trying to satisfy by increased intake of food. She may even request peculiar dishes at odd hours, seemingly selected to test the patience and concern of the accommodating husband. But if overweight is caused by uncontrolled intake, it is up to the husband and the physician to seek out the causes and correct them.

The baby will not suffer if the mother's hunger is not totally satisfied, provided her diet is adequate. Conversely, it is possible for the mother to be overfed and undernourished. Usually it is best for the mother to continue her regular normal diet, without desserts. The question of *how much milk* finds disagreement among obstetricians. Although milk is a natural food supplement, heavy quantities of it may lead to weight problems. A mineral-vitamin capsule once or twice daily continuing until two or three months after delivery (especially if the mother is to nurse her baby) may serve the nutritional requirements of pregnancy without increased weight.

Related to diet is bowel function. Because pregnancy disrupts the functions of some of the abdominal organs, most women find an occasional need for a mild laxative. Enemas are not recommended, except in unusual circumstances, for they may disturb the uterus.

Breast-feeding

At the initial visit to the obstetrician the woman is asked whether she prefers to nurse her baby. Many women wish to, some are not so sure and postpone a decision. A small number seem to have an aversion to the nursing act for a variety of reasons—from misunderstanding to deep-seated psychological problems. The obstetrician may recommend that a woman try nursing, because only by experiencing it can she become aware of the emotional satisfaction that it may have. Nursing is without question the best thing for the baby.

Some women are unnecessarily worried because they think that nursing will change the shape of the breasts. The breasts enlarge during pregnancy, and milk comes into them (*lactation*) after delivery. Even if breast-feeding is not practiced, the resulting swelling and congestion that remain until the suppression of lactation, usually by hormone medication, will have much the same effect on the breast contours as feeding itself.

This is perhaps a good time for the obstetrician to remind the expectant mother that bearing children exacts a varying toll in physical appearance and condition. We hear of the woman who has borne many children and still keeps her trim, attractive figure, but even those who seem to be lucky pay the biological price to some extent. It can be lessened by good obstetrical care and cooperation in utilizing it. The birth of a child and the joy of family fulfillment should more than offset such considerations.

Clothing

Loose clothing is recommended for better circulation as are low- or medium-heel shoes for better support, but unless there is some demonstrable need, maternity belts and corsets are not. It is better to have the back and abdominal muscles assume their own job of supporting the increasing weight of the enlarging uterus to condition them for their role in labor and delivery. A stretch girdle will give all the support that is needed.

Sleep

The bodily changes brought about by pregnancy may produce unusual fatigue. The obstetrician assures the woman that she may need extra rest at night and periodic rest or naps during the day. He can point out that the mother owes this rest to herself and her child. A fatigued and overworked mother finds it difficult to enjoy her pregnancy and her other family relationships.

Sexual Relations

At the first visit the question of intercourse during pregnancy is explained. In the early stages of pregnancy, relations are permitted as desired, with extra gentleness suggested around the time the menstrual period would otherwise fall due. If at any time the patient notices staining, bleeding, pain, cramps, or anything unusual during or following intercourse, she is advised to discontinue sexual activities until she can discuss the symptoms with her obstetrician.

Relations should become less frequent and more gentle as the pregnancy progresses. They should cease altogether about six weeks before the expected time of delivery. It is then that the cervix becomes softer, much congested with blood, and somewhat irritable, as are the labia and vaginal membranes. To avoid damage to these tissues, or possible premature occurrence of labor, it is best to discontinue relations entirely. In any event, some women, particularly as the pregnancy advances, do not enjoy the act, and men may be less sexually stimulated by their wives as the shape of the body changes. If there is an uneven loss of sexual appetite, it is best for the spouses to discuss this openly to seek an acceptable solution. Under normal conditions, sexual relations are not resumed until six weeks after the birth of the baby.

Travel

Travel is permissible, mostly in the early months of pregnancy, but it is best avoided when the menstrual period would otherwise occur. At that time if a journey is essential, it should be divided into short trips, especially if the vehicle is an automobile. Long, jarring, fatiguing rides can disturb pregnancies.

When long distances are necessary, the fast, less tiring airplane is preferable. But long trips at high altitudes are discouraged, for although cabins are pressurized, the question of oxygen supply for the fetus is important. In the absence of reliable information about altitude and pregnancy, a flight of about six hours is suggested, more or less arbitrarily, as a maximum.

"Moderation in All Things"

The golden rule of pregnancy is moderation in all things. It applies to smoking, drinking, dancing, and exercise. Another problem is how long to continue to work. It depends on how strenuous and exhausting the work might be. Clerical workers and teachers, for instance, might be able to continue through the sixth or seventh month. Each case has to be judged separately according to the nature of the work and the physical and emotional needs of the patient.

Fees

A bothersome but necessary point discussed at the initial visit is the obstetrical fee. This is usually all-inclusive, covering care from the initial visit to the end of the six-week recovery period. It includes laboratory tests and delivery. The number and spacing of visits are determined by the patient's needs and symptoms. The first six months commonly require one visit each four weeks, plus occasional phone calls. During the seventh and eighth months visits are made every two weeks, and during the last month weekly or more frequently.

As part of this same discussion the patient is told about hospital arrangements and costs. The obstetrician inquires into the financial status of the patient, medical group plans, if any, and tries to arrange things so that there is a minimum financial burden. The patient is encouraged to talk frankly about money matters so that a clear and satisfactory arrangement will be reached and future misunderstandings avoided.

Distress Signals

At the first meeting, the obstetrician also acquaints the woman with signs of potential threats to the pregnancy—staining or bleeding, uterine cramps or severe backaches—and what to do about them should they appear. Some women will occasionally stain during pregnancy, especially when their menstrual periods would otherwise occur; others will even have some menstrual flow and still remain pregnant. But they are the exceptions.

However, there are frequently other causes for staining. An irritated cervix may bleed spontaneously or after intercourse. A low implantation in the uterus is another cause. At any rate, at the first sign of staining or cramps a patient is advised to call the obstetrician and stay in bed until told otherwise. Most cases of staining will clear up with simple and conservative care, but the patient will have to refrain from sexual relations for one to two weeks and avoid strenuous activities at the times her menstrual period would normally fall due.

During this same discussion the mother is told of her role in providing nourishment for the child and of the influence her health has on his. She is warned of the toxic effects of infections or drugs which she might transmit to the child; she is advised to avoid exposure to communicable diseases, and to have all diseases (including infected teeth) treated as quickly as possible.

Training for Childbirth

Toward the end of the first visit, the patient is given literature on maternal health and infant care. The booklets have answers to many of the same points discussed during the initial meeting. So much must be accomplished at this meeting that elaboration and reinforcement through more leisurely reading is desirable. The patient is advised to show some of the reading to her husband, and maybe to bring him along on a subsequent visit to meet the obstetrician. Husband and doctor can talk about cooperating in the care of the patient whose welfare is entrusted to both of them. The husband may also have some questions to which he can get no satisfactory answers from his wife or from reading. He is thus made to feel that he is more than merely an accessory to the fact.

Attending classes on pregnancy and childbirth is recommended. A number of hospitals and maternity centers give classes in "natural childbirth," which attempt to reduce fear and pain through knowledge and through a series of exercises to keep the muscles of the body in good tone for labor and delivery. The husband should attend some classes, if possible, to gain a better concept of his role in relation to his wife's experiences. Man and wife are brought closer together, and this aids the wife considerably in achieving the feeling of security that is so important to her at this time.

Finally the patient is told to feel free to call the obstetrician if anything disturbs her, and she is assured that in the unlikely event of an emergency, arrangements will have been made for her at the hospital. She can go there directly and be cared for until the obstetrician arrives. She is also advised to keep a list of questions that come to her mind between visits, and to bring it for discussion next time.

The initial visit to the obstetrician is obviously of prime importance, particularly for a woman bearing a first child, and consumes much time. The visit should never be rushed. But even the veteran mother forgets, and likes the reassurance of competence, patience, and understanding. Although at this stage the child within the mother is still tiny, he soon becomes the cause of much special attention that ought to be well guided and meaningful to her.

Fetus

The last twenty-eight weeks before delivery are known as the fetal stage. The change from embryonal to fetal life is not abrupt; it is marked for the most part by an increase in the size of the child and by refinement in the details of body structures and accessory organs to the birth.

Placenta

By the early part of the fourth month after conception only the villi next to the uterine wall remain and are henceforth known as the placenta. The placenta continues the function of the villi, serving as the site for interchange of nutrition from the mother to the fetus, and of wastes from the fetus to the mother. The food substances in the mother's blood are drawn by osmosis into the placental circulation, and conducted by the umbilical cord to the fetus. The placenta is not unlike a very fine screen which admits fluids, salts, most proteins, and unfortunately, some viruses but usually stops such larger substances as blood cells and most bacteria. The placenta also manufactures most of the hormone that maintains a healthful pregnancy.

The portion of the chorionic membrane from which the villi have disappeared, together with the placenta, form the outer wall of the sac within which the fetus develops. The sac is filled with fluid and grows and distends rapidly enough to insure free movement of the fetus. The fluid also acts as a protective buffer against injury from a direct blow or from abnormal pressure exerted on the mother's abdomen.

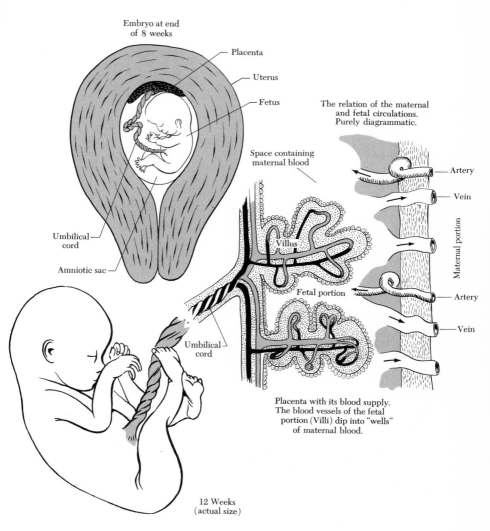

Embryo at end
of 8 weeks

Placenta

Uterus

Fetus

The relation of the maternal
and fetal circulations.
Purely diagrammatic.

Space containing
maternal blood

Artery

Vein

Umbilical
cord

Maternal portion

Villus

Amniotic sac

Fetal portion

Artery

Vein

Umbilical
cord

Placenta with its blood supply.
The blood vessels of the fetal
portion (Villi) dip into "wells"
of maternal blood.

12 Weeks
(actual size)

FIGURE 11. *Fetal development.*

Umbilical Cord and Amniotic Sac

While the placenta and chorionic membrane have been developing, two other important accessory structures have been growing simultaneously—the umbilical cord, which forms a connective conduit between fetus and placenta, and the amniotic sac, whose wall eventually forms a lining over the inner surface of the chorionic membrane and placenta.

The umbilical cord is essentially the body stalk grown longer and thinner. It is about two inches long after three months, twenty inches long at birth. It is highly elastic and twisted by inequality in the length of the blood vessels composing it. The amniotic sac is filled with fluid, about one quart at the time of birth, and completely surrounds the embryo except at the point of attachment (umbilicus) to the umbilical cord.

Outward Signs of Pregnancy

During the fourth month, the growth of the fetus necessitates more rapid enlargement of the uterus, which in turn causes increasing protrusion of the mother's lower abdomen. The uterus comes up out of the pelvis proper into the lower abdomen and can easily be felt through the abdominal wall. It is reassuring for the mother to feel this herself. By the end of the fourth month, it is midway to the umbilicus. A few weeks later she will experience butterfly or gas bubble sensations in her abdomen—first at wide intervals but soon more often. These are the early fetal movements that will become more regular and slightly stronger. These movements are a great source of emotional satisfaction; the mother is aware of her baby and feels secure that it is growing and doing well. This is the beginning of the intimate association between mother and child.

Some weeks after life is felt, it is possible to hear the tiny fetal heartbeat. Both heartbeat and movements soon become stronger and more active, and movements can be observed on the abdomen. The mother and father usually enjoy feeling and seeing them—even when they are occasionally awakened by them in the middle of the night.

When the fetal heartbeat is loud enough to be heard easily, the obstetrician lets the mother listen through the stethoscope. At first, the mother's face shows concentration in the effort to hear: she

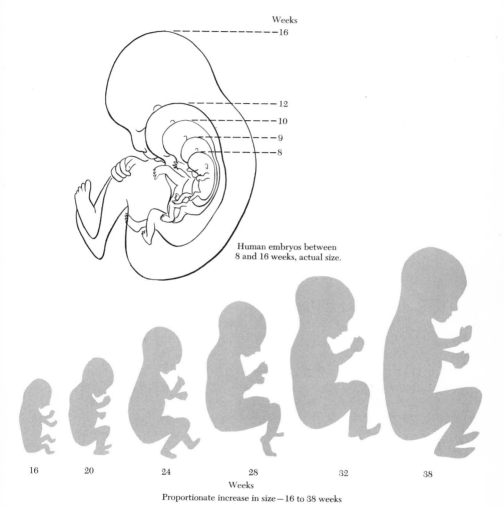

Weeks
16

12
10
9
8

Human embryos between
8 and 16 weeks, actual size.

16   20   24   28   32   38

Weeks

Proportionate increase in size—16 to 38 weeks

FIGURE 12. *Growth of the fetus.*

53

shakes her head, *no;* but as she continues to listen and becomes used to the extraneous noises she finally hears the fetal heart softly beating in the background. At this point a smile spreads across her face and a look of joy and satisfaction dispels the intense concentration. She is surprised at the rapid rate of the fetal heart and is assured that 140 to 160 beats a minute are normal, although twice that of an adult.

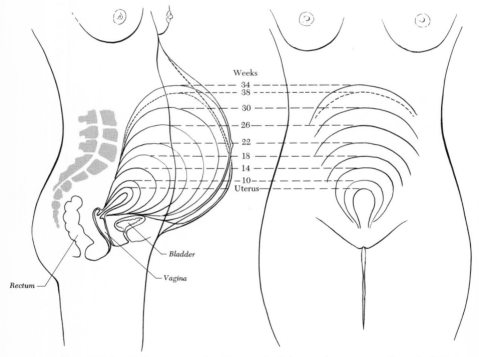

FIGURE 13.   *Enlargement of uterus and abdomen between tenth and thirty-eighth weeks of pregnancy.*

During the early fetal period the woman's figure begins to show that she is pregnant. As we have said, starting about the fourth month, her lower abdomen protrudes and becomes rounded, her breasts gradually increase in size and she gives other signs of a general increase in weight. It is during this period especially that she should be reading, attending classes, and exercising so that she will know what is going on within her body and preparing herself psychologically and physically for delivery. This is probably the most comfortable time of pregnancy, with only occasional constipation, leg cramp, or fatigue, which can readily be corrected by diet and rest, or, now and then, medication.

Her visits to the obstetrician have at this point become routine. Her blood pressure and weight are taken, and her uterus felt through the abdominal wall; a specimen urine is checked. Her extremities are examined for swelling, and she is questioned about bowel movements and such possible difficulties as headaches, backaches, or vaginal discharges.

Miscarriage

In this period the woman is less apprehensive about losing the baby. She has become used to her condition, continues to gain confidence as things proceed well, and starts to relax and enjoy it all. Unfortunately, however, a few cases of pregnancy will terminate here. Sometimes the cause of the miscarriage can be determined, but more often it cannot. The loss of the baby at this time, after it has been felt to be alive, anticipated and identified with, is discouraging to all concerned. A time of depression and sadness has to be lived through. If women who undergo this sort of an experience know that such a reaction is normal they endure it more effectively. Most reassuring, however, is the fact that subsequent pregnancies may follow an uncomplicated course; the couple should be so advised if this appears to be the outlook for them.

Tales of Complications

As the outward signs of pregnancy appear, people will begin to comment. Occasionally, some of them subject a woman to a sadistic ritual. While assuring her that of course it won't happen in her case, they tell tales of abnormal babies born to their close friends or relatives. They recite with apparent relish case histories, of which they have first hand knowledge, of complications in delivery and extensive surgery. They remember unfortunate friends who died in childbirth. These are rare cases, but happen just often enough to give some credence to their stories—but not much.

The pregnant woman, however, may be disturbed enough to

need reassurance. She should be encouraged to talk out her fears, and made to realize that most pregnant women have some, and that she should not feel sheepish or childish in talking about hers. Then she should be informed that "monster" stories are highly exaggerated, and that the overwhelming majority of births are uncomplicated and yield normal, healthy children. Most embryos which would be born with abnormal characteristics are spontaneously aborted—nature's way of discarding the unfit. Birth itself can generally be taken as a stamp of approval by nature, certifying that the individual is qualified to face life. The vast improvements in obstetrical and hospital procedures are good insurance against severe complications at birth, and death of the mother in childbirth is rare.

However, the mother should be reminded of the forces that do influence the developing child and of her role in these.

Physical Influences on the Developing Child

Many characteristics of the child are fixed at the instant of conception, through heredity, and cannot be changed. Since there is no direct blood or nerve connection between the mother and the developing child, myths about birthmarks and other deformities in the child alleged to be caused by something a mother saw or thought during pregnancy are unfounded. Birth marks are caused by abnormal localized development of the child's skin and are not related to the mental and emotional state of the mother. However, she should be reminded of her influential role as a protector and nourisher, and that an inadequate food and vitamin supply may harm the child. She should also, as we have said, keep in good physical condition and avoid excessive smoking or drinking. Nicotine and alcohol, as well as other narcotics and drugs, have adverse effects on the child. Low-weight and premature babies may be the result of the mother's heavy smoking.

Certain disease germs and viruses, notably those of German measles, typhoid, influenza, diphtheria, and syphilis, may also reach the child with harmful effect. The negative influence of German measles in the first three months of pregnancy on the sight and hearing of the child has long been known. But now there is increasing evidence that embryo and fetal abnormalities are more often than suspected due to the toxic effects of infection or drugs transmitted to the child by the mother. Indeed, depending on when the toxic impact takes place, it is almost possible to predict which defect will be found. It is now also thought that many other disease conditions, which are mild to the mother, might nevertheless be toxic to the growing fetus. Viruses and bacterial infections of colds, and intestinal and kidney diseases are certainly to be avoided and, if contracted during pregnancy, treated with special attention.

Babies born with a disease such as syphilis led at one time to the belief that a communicable disease could be inherited. Actually no sperm or egg cell could carry a disease germ of any kind and function. It is likely that the mother was infected before or during pregnancy and the disease transmitted to the fetus through the placental barrier. The mother who is cured of syphilis, cures the baby within her at the same time. If treatment is started early enough in pregnancy the child can be born free of the disease.

Whether a child's disease is inherited or acquired within the uterus (*congenital*) is very important. If a congenital condition like syphilis is cured the child—no matter how diseased its parents were —can grow to healthy maturity, marry, and have children without the slightest fear that the condition will be transmitted. But if a defect is inherited, no matter whether it is cured or not, and no matter how healthy the individual himself may be when he marries, there is always the possibility that he may pass on the disease through his genes. Such things as six fingers on a hand and tendencies toward diabetes and allergies may appear in later descendants.

Rh Factor

The mother may have to be told about the Rh factor if the prenatal blood test reveals she is Rh negative. The Rh factor has received increasing attention and publicity in recent years as a cause of spontaneous abortion and of diseases such as cerebral palsy, mental retardation, and deafness.

Rh is the symbol for an inherited protein substance found in human red blood cells. It stands for rhesus because it was first detected in rhesus monkeys. The Rh factor is present in the blood of about 85 per cent of white people making them Rh positive. The 15 per cent who do not have it are Rh negative. An even higher percentage of people of other racial backgrounds are Rh positive: 93 per cent of Negroes and 99 per cent of Chinese, for example.

A blood sample is taken from the mother during her first visit to the obstetrician. If it is Rh negative, a blood sample is taken from her husband as well. The Rh protein has nothing to do with the quality of the blood. There are, however, certain parental combinations of Rh factors which may cause difficulty for the child.

There has been a lot of needless worry about the Rh factor. There is no danger of any kind if both mother and father are Rh positive, or if both are Rh negative. There are only slight dangers when the mother has Rh positive blood and the father is Rh negative. A possibility of trouble exists when the mother is Rh negative and the father, Rh positive. Even then, no problem exists if the child inherits the mother's Rh negative blood—which is what happens in almost half the cases.

The Rh positive father may be either *homozygous*, in which case all his children will be Rh positive, or he may be *heterozygous* so that there is an even chance that any child will be Rh negative. Special blood tests can show which he is. It happens this way: one of each pair of genes for a certain trait comes from a person's father and one from his mother. The Rh factor is a dominant trait—if one of the pair of genes is positive, the person will be Rh positive. If both the father's genes are positive (homozygous) only positive genes can be passed on, and all the children will be Rh positive. On the other hand, a man who has one positive and one negative Rh gene (heterozygous) will have positive blood, but can pass either a positive or negative gene to any given child. If his wife is Rh negative, both of her genes will be negative. Thus there is an even chance that a child will receive an Rh negative gene from his father, and have Rh negative blood.

A chance of danger is present only when the child inherits his father's Rh positive blood type. This causes the mother's negative system to produce antibodies against the baby's blood. In spite of the lack of direct connection—the placental barrier—a few cells of the baby's blood get into the mother's bloodstream. Her body then produces antibodies to destroy the baby's blood cells and the Rh protein they contain. These antibodies make their way back through the placental barrier to the child's bloodstream and tend to destroy his red blood cells.

There is little if any difficulty with the first child. The mother's blood apparently doesn't develop enough antibodies to cause serious

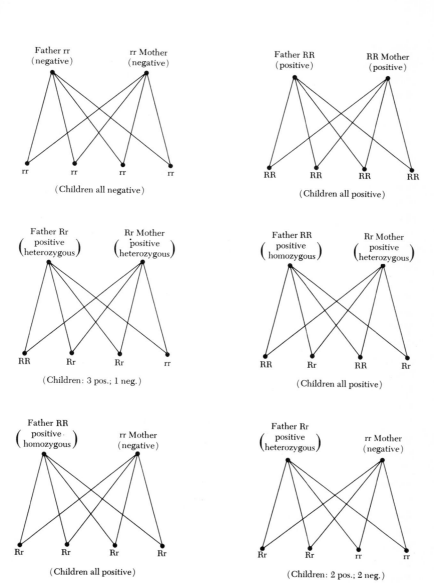

Father rr
(negative)

rr Mother
(negative)

rr   rr   rr   rr

(Children all negative)

Father RR
(positive)

RR Mother
(positive)

RR   RR   RR   RR

(Children all positive)

Father Rr
(positive
heterozygous)

Rr Mother
(positive
heterozygous)

RR   Rr   Rr   rr

(Children: 3 pos.; 1 neg.)

Father RR
(positive
homozygous)

Rr Mother
(positive
heterozygous)

RR   Rr   RR   Rr

(Children all positive)

Father RR
(positive
homozygous)

rr Mother
(negative)

Rr   Rr   Rr   Rr

(Children all positive)

Father Rr
(positive
heterozygous)

rr Mother
(negative)

Rr   Rr   rr   rr

(Children: 2 pos.; 2 neg.)

FIGURE 14.   *Transmission of Rh factor.*

trouble. But it may do so if she becomes pregnant several times with an Rh positive child. The destruction of red blood cells causes anemia or progressive jaundice. These conditions may be mild and curable, but in severe cases the child's blood cells may be destroyed at a rapid rate, and he may be born dead, either prematurely or near the expected date of delivery. In such extreme cases the physician might advise the couple against further pregnancies.

Obstetricians are now alert to Rh dangers. They periodically determine the concentration of antibodies in the mother's blood, and watch particularly for any marked or sudden increase in concentration, a sure sign of trouble. In any case, they are ready to test the baby's blood at birth and/or periodically thereafter to determine if he needs an exchange transfusion of Rh negative blood. Here a large percentage of the baby's Rh positive blood cells are removed, and replaced by Rh negative cells from a donor's blood, which will not be affected by the antibodies.

During the course of an exchange transfusion a small amount of the baby's blood is removed, and an equal amount of donor blood given—a process that is repeated about fifty times. The transfusion takes about two hours. The danger, which depends largely on the condition of the infant, is never great but always present.

In view of the great help offered by medical science, it is rare today for a woman to be advised against pregnancy because of the Rh factor. Certainly the Rh blood type should never be a decisive factor in any couple's decision about starting a family.

The Late Fetal Stage

As the fetal period moves along, the mother-to-be grows more uncomfortable. Some women tend to develop trouble with their veins (varicosities), which get larger and more troublesome with each pregnancy. The veins may be superficial, the so-called "spider type" varicosities, or they may be large and deep, on the labia, legs, and thighs. Elastic stockings or bandages for severe cases may be of some help and are frequently recommended. At the same time the woman is advised not to wear any tight or constricting garters, which can impede circulation and further distend the veins. Some of the varicosities may be located in the hemorrhoid ring around the anal opening, where they are a troublesome nuisance as the preg-

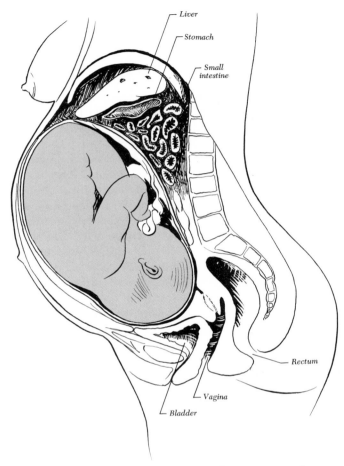

FIGURE 15. *Late fetal stage showing crowding of maternal organs.*

nancy progresses. This is one reason constipation is particularly to be avoided during pregnancy.

During the last three months before delivery, the patient sees the obstetrician more often, and her health and symptoms are followed closely, for it is during this period that some serious complications may develop.

The uterus by this time has extended into the upper abdomen, stretching the abdominal wall, sometimes creating silver stretch marks in the skin of the lower abdomen. The intestines and stomach are pushed higher and toward the side and back. The fetal movements are now strong and active, and occasionally cause some discomfort in the upper abdomen. The woman may experience "heart-burn" or indigestion from pressure on the stomach. This can also cause a delay in emptying the stomach by interfering with peristal-sis. In the last month, the uterus will spread the lower ribs and create pressure on the diaphragm, causing shallowness of breath-ing, and limiting the movement of the diaphragm so that chest colds and coughs are more difficult to clear up. But two or three weeks before delivery the baby's head moves down into the pelvis (*lighten-ing*), and there is some relief of pressure symptoms in the upper ab-domen. These may simply be traded, however, for pressure symp-toms in the pelvis, depending on the size of the pelvis in relation to the size and position of the fetal head. Bladder irritability, constipa-tion, and a general heaviness in the pelvis itself will sometimes be felt. It is at this stage that women who have had three or more chil-dren sometimes feel that "everything is going to fall out." Pressure on the nerves and blood vessels that run along the inner walls of the bony pelvis may cause cramps or pains in the legs, and some heaviness and swelling particularly if the woman is on her feet long hours.

At the time of lightening, the activity of the baby will be some-what curtailed, causing some women to wonder if all is well. It is, however, a normal development and should cause no alarm. About this time some physicians re-examine and evaluate the pelvis to estimate the size of the pelvis in relation to the head of the child.

The mother should wear sensible shoes to get all possible foot and leg support for carrying the added weight. There is a slight softening of the hips and other bony structures that make up the pelvis. Not only is balance more difficult to maintain, but a fall could be disastrous. Because of the weight of the enlarged uterus, the stretched abdominal walls and muscles, especially the back muscles, are put under a strain. The mother has to compensate for the heavy protuberant abdomen in her posture and walk; she leans slightly backward, with shoulders thrown back somewhat. This gives her what Shakespeare called the "proud strut of pregnancy." If her back aches in spite of a good program of exercise, then heat, massage and a firm mattress may help.

During the last month it is not exceptional for the woman to remain steady in weight or even lose a few pounds. She feels awk-ward and unwieldy, time seems to drag, and she welcomes instruction in the signs and symptoms of labor to end her nine months of childbearing. At the same time her fear of delivery may increase a bit, as may a more diffuse fear of parting with the fetus.

Thirty-nine weeks after conception is the most common time for birth. Eighty-one per cent of all births occur between thirty-six and forty-two weeks after conception. Another 9 per cent fall between the thirty-first and thirty-fifth weeks. Fifty-two per cent of all birth mortalities occur to those born earlier than thirty-one weeks after conception and two-thirds to those born prior to the thirty-sixth week. Premature babies' chances for survival are not simply indicated by their gestational age—seven-month baby—but also by their weight. This combined index is also likely to provide clues to the deficiencies they will suffer, and methods for treating them. The lowest mortality rate appears between the thirty-sixth and fortieth weeks; it rises again after forty-two weeks.

The fetus ready for delivery weighs about six to eight pounds with smaller and larger babies not uncommon. All organs are sufficiently mature to maintain life without dependence on the mother's body. The transition entails a hazardous journey to the outside, and some marked circulatory changes are necessary so that the infant can breathe his own oxygen, digest his own food, and excrete his own waste. But it should be emphasized that since conception the child has had systems for these functions without direct connection to the systems of his mother. At birth he simply disconnects aid from her and exists on his own. In many ways he is just as much a human being before birth as afterward. It will surely seem so to the mother who has nurtured him from a single cell to someone large enough to distort her body, who has felt him live within her, and who has had so much of her life directed toward meeting his needs.

labor and delivery

Labor is accomplished in three stages. The first starts with the early signs of labor and ends when the cervix of the uterus is open enough to allow the baby to pass through. This stage lasts from six to eighteen hours or longer with the first baby, and from three to ten hours for subsequent babies. The second stage begins when the cervix of the uterus is fully open, and ends when the baby is born. It lasts from twenty minutes to two hours or longer. The third stage, ending with the delivery of the afterbirth (placenta, amniotic sac, and chorionic membrane), lasts about fifteen to thirty minutes.

First Stage

The first or cervical stage of labor is accomplished by uterine contractions which gradually stretch, thin out, and dilate the cervical canal, helping to start the head of the child through the birth canal.

The exact mechanism that determines the onset of labor is unknown. Most probably it relates to the level of hormones in the mother's blood which increases the irritability of the uterus. Or it may be that the extreme distension of the uterus itself brings on contractions. Occasionally, even the activity of the mother or her mental state—e.g., fear, shock—may influence the onset of labor.

In the nonpregnant state, the uterus undergoes gentle rhythmic contractions with frequencies from a few to as many as eight or more a minute. These become stronger and more noticeable as the menstrual period approaches, and are felt by most women as mild contractions or cramps at the approach of the menstrual flow. The uterus also contracts rhythmically and mildly all during pregnancy and so maintains its muscle tone. In the last four to six weeks before delivery, the mother may become more aware of these contractions, and they can grow to proportions which lead her to wonder whether she is entering the first stage of labor. These false labor pains have been responsible for many unnecessary midnight dashes to the hospital. Such contractions are a sign of an increasing irritability of the uterine muscle which will continue until real labor begins, and are quite normal.

Three reliable symptoms help to identify true labor: nature of the contractions, appearance of the "show," and rupture of the bag of waters.

Nature of Contractions

In actual labor the woman will be conscious of some sensation in the lower back and abdomen and notice a simultaneous hardening of the uterus. As the contraction subsides, the uterus grows soft again. At the beginning, the contractions may be from fifteen to

FIGURE 16. *Fetus at full term.*

FIGURE 17. *First stage of labor.*

FIGURE 18. *Second stage of labor.*

twenty or more minutes apart, but gradually they come regularly and more frequently. They start in the back, and gradually work their way around to the front. The pains, at first mild, intensify with successive contractions, and last from about half a minute initially to a minute or longer toward the end.

"Show"

A second sign of the advent of labor is the discharge of the slightly bloody cervical mucus plug ("show"). During the development of the child within the mother (*gestation*), the canal of the cervix is filled with a tenacious plug of mucus that acts like a soft cork and prevents infections from entering the uterine cavity. At the onset of labor, and sometimes even before labor contractions start, the cervix softens and stretches enough to release this plug. It sometimes contains slight streaks of blood from the softened walls and membranes of the cervix, such as mucus blown from the nose will occasionally contain. The discharge of this plug indicates that the uterus is getting ready to start labor within the next twenty-four hours.

Bag of Waters

A third symptom of approaching labor is the rupture (sometimes slow or partial but usually full) of the bag of waters within which the baby has been growing, and a consequent gush of water from the vagina. If the bag ruptures before or early in the first stage, the labor will be dry. This may entail a slightly prolonged labor, particularly with the first child, but is not very much of a problem today. The bag of waters does play a slight part in the early dilation of the cervix. After this its importance is doubtful—so much so that occasionally, if labor is not progressing as desired, the physician will rupture these membranes and allow the fluid or some part of it to escape. With the release of the fluid (from a cupful to a quart) the uterus will become slightly smaller in size, and the muscles might contract more powerfully and more frequently. As a rule the bag of waters ruptures spontaneously during the first or second stage, and the labor then progresses more actively. If the membranes do not rupture of themselves, the head of the child will descend behind what is called a bag of forewaters, which will be broken by the obstetrician before the head of the baby is delivered. If for any reason this does not happen, the baby will be born with the membranes (*caul* or *veil*) over the head. At one time this was thought to be a good luck omen for the baby, and the caul was sought, especially by superstitious mariners, as a charm to ward off drowning.

As soon as the bag of waters ruptures, it is best for the woman to go immediately to the hospital where she will be under competent supervision. The reason for this is twofold. If the fetal head is not well engaged in the pelvis during the gush of water from the uterus, the umbilical cord may slip down alongside the head into the vagina. Pressure on this cord by the descending head may stop circulation through the cord and endanger the baby. The other reason is to avoid the possibility of an ascending infection in the uterus and fetal sac.

If any of the three signs of labor manifests itself, the woman should, with reasonable haste, ask her obstetrician about going to the hospital. She should have an overnight bag packed and ready to go.

Since women are naturally apprehensive about the first experience of childbirth, it is sometimes helpful if they know what to expect at the hospital. It is even advisable for them to tour the hospital ahead of time to learn as much as possible first hand about labor, delivery, and lying-in rooms, and other facilities they will use during their period of confinement. Most hospitals have a well-trained staff in the obstetrical division, including not only the woman's own physician, but resident physicians in training, nurses specially skilled in obstetrics, and an anesthetist. It is best to let this team, of which the woman herself should become a member, assume, or at least share her concern as much as possible. They are specialists in such situations, and "have travelled the road many times." She should let them take over.

At the hospital, her clothes are taken, hospital gowns substituted, charts made out, temperature taken, baby's heart listened to and recorded. Questions are asked about the onset of labor and type of contractions, which will now be timed. Anything out of the ordinary is reported immediately to her physician, or whoever is substituting temporarily. She is made comfortable, and the nurses attempt to establish a climate of warmth and reassurance. The woman usually recognizes that she is in capable hands, and relaxes with confidence to the job ahead.

She is then prepared for delivery. The pubic area is shaved for hygienic reasons, and she is generally given an enema to clean out the lower bowel tract so that soiling of the delivery area by mother's stool will be minimized when the baby is born; the enema also seems to have a stimulating effect on the uterine contractions in the early stages of labor. Once these procedures are out of the way, the patient settles down to the progress of labor itself. In the early stages there is little discomfort, and she can rest, read, and even walk about. Later she will be moved to the labor room. At some hospitals, husbands are welcome in the labor room to comfort the wife. When this happens, they emerge with a healthy respect for the work associated with childbearing.

When labor starts, the rim of the cervix and the descending fetal head can be felt quite easily either through the rectal wall of the mother by the educated finger of the obstetrician or by vaginal examination. At the beginning of labor the cervix is about one finger dilated. As labor progresses the rim of the cervix dilates to about four fingers and then fully. This completes the first stage of labor, and the head of the child, which has been descending further and further into the pelvis, now completely fills it.

It is in the later stages of cervical dilation that the woman will begin to experience her greatest discomfort. The physician may give a mild sedative when necessary plus a pain-controlling drug to make the contractions less uncomfortable. However, drugs must be used judiciously for they may prolong labor, or make the mother restless and uncooperative. If drugs are given too close to the time of birth, the baby may be born sluggish and have some difficulty starting to breathe. Usually with the onset of the second stage of labor the pains become different. They are stronger, last longer and come more frequently. The mother feels like bearing down with each pain as though it were necessary to move the bowels.

Second Stage

The second or pushing stage of labor is usually much shorter than the first, lasting from twenty minutes to an hour or two, with variations. The diaphragm, back, and abdominal muscles assist the strong uterine contractions (and at times vigorous and uncomfortable bearing down efforts by the mother) to bring the fetal head to the vaginal opening, where it can be assisted out by the obstetrician. At this point a woman having her first baby needs the guidance and encouragement of nurses and physicians to use her contractions and bearing down efforts most effectively. She may fear injury to herself by pushing a large baby through what up to now has been a narrow canal. Without good obstetrical help she might tear and injure the tissues and muscles of the outlet and damage or stretch the deeper fibrous tissues that hold and support the bladder and rectum. But she is assured that competent help is on hand and urged to go ahead with her efforts.

In the last part of the second stage, the baby's head pushes against the vaginal opening and the muscles surrounding it. With each contraction the region between the rectal opening and lips of the vagina (*perineum*) bulges and then relaxes as the head of the child first moves forward and then retracts as the contraction subsides. Shortly after this, the baby's head will increasingly dilate the vaginal opening each time contractions move it forward, and soon the scalp (*caput*) can be seen.

At this point the woman will go to the delivery room. She is placed on the delivery table with her legs in obstetrical stirrups, exposing the pelvic outlet and making it easier for the obstetrician to assist in the delivery of the child. In order to protect the pelvic tissues, the woman having her first baby will probably be incised through the rear edge of the vaginal wall (*episiotomy*), in the midline or off to one side of the rectum. Making a clean surgical incision that can easily be repaired is better than permitting the tissues to stretch and probably tear. At the time the episiotomy is performed, the patient is given either a whiff of gas or a local anesthetic injection.

With gentle traction and guidance on the part of the obstetrician, the baby's head is then delivered through the dilated vagina. The head is slightly moldable because the bony structures of the skull have not yet fully united. This is the largest part of the child which passes through the birth canal, and it is quickly followed by the body.

The baby, though clear of the birth canal, is not yet free of the umbilical cord to the placenta, which is still attached to the uterine

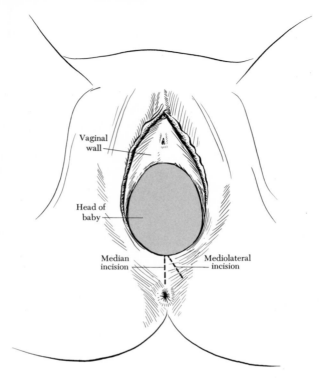

FIGURE 19.   *Episiotomy.*

wall. The exact stimulus that starts the baby breathing is not known, but as soon as he is born he cries and establishes his own respiration. The obstetrician holds the baby upside down to facilitate the drainage and removal of mucus from his mouth and throat. The umbilical cord is then doubly clamped about one to two inches from the navel of the baby and severed between the clamps. The cord is either tied or a small metal or elastic clamp is applied. A dressing is then placed over the stump of the umbilical cord remaining with the child. This portion eventually dries up and drops off, and the point of final attachment is known as the umbilicus or navel. After the cord is cut, a sample of blood from the maternal cut end is tested to determine if Rh antibodies are present to a hazardous extent in the baby's blood. The second stage of labor has ended.

The baby is placed in a warming crib in the delivery room,

cleaned, and identified by a bracelet, necklace, and/or fingerprints and footprints. A fresh solution of 1 per cent silver nitrate or some other effective medicant is put into the baby's eyes to prevent infection.

While the infant is being cared for by the nurses and physicians who assisted in the delivery, the obstetrician repairs the episiotomy and awaits the third stage of labor—the expulsion of the afterbirth. At this point the mother may begin to experience exultant and euphoric feelings; these may be followed by a mild depression, usually lasting for a short period of time. In a small fraction of cases, however, the depression is severe and long lasting. While these states probably have emotional roots, they also seem to relate to the abrupt endocrine changes that occur subsequent to delivery; there is a marked drop in estrogen and progesterone in her circulating blood.

Third Stage

The third stage consists of the separation and expulsion of the afterbirth (placenta, amniotic sac, chorionic membranes) from the uterus. This usually occurs within twenty minutes of the delivery of the child. Assisted by the contractions of the now much smaller uterus, and sometimes by pressure applied by the obstetrician on the uterus, the placenta separates from its position of implantation on the wall of the uterus. It is usually delivered intact, with the membranes, with little difficulty or pain to the mother, but with a small amount of bleeding precipitated by the separation.

To prevent excessive bleeding and to help contract the uterus the patient may be given a drug such as ergot or posterior pituitary solution. The afterbirth is examined by the physician to make sure it has separated properly and to uncover any signs of disease in the placenta. The uterus is checked for firmness and contraction and signs of abnormal bleeding. The pelvic area is cleansed, the legs are lowered from the obstetrical stirrups, and the mother is allowed to rest before returning to her room.

We have described the uncomplicated delivery of a first child. Subsequent deliveries are ordinarily shorter and somewhat easier, but not always.

Labor and delivery are physiological aspects of an experience

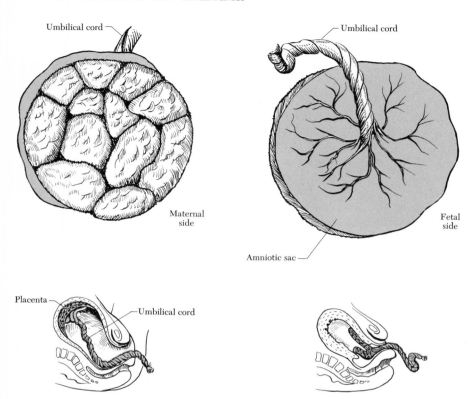

FIGURE 20. *Third stage of labor showing both sides of placenta.*

that normally goes from beginning to end without inordinate discomfort or complication. However, many women are unprepared
for the hard work required in the second stage of labor and delivery.
Unfortunately, the very experience set up to establish a realistic
understanding of this process sometimes works in reverse. Mothers
attend classes in natural childbirth to gain a better understanding
of the physiology and mechanics of labor. They also engage in
prescribed exercises to improve body tone for less painful, more
efficient labor and delivery. They may also see one of the excellent
films of the actual birth of a baby. Although such preparation is
recommended and helpful, women are sometimes left with the
erroneous idea that if they exercise, breathe right, think nice

thoughts, conquer their fears, and behave like ladies, they will have a simple, easy delivery, with labor pains they will barely feel. But such deliveries, though possible for some women, are unlikely for most. They are amazed, irritated, and disappointed at encountering long, hard, and uncomfortable labor. They may feel they have been misled by the devotees of natural childbirth. Even worse, a woman may feel she has failed herself and her obstetrician. She frequently apologizes to him for the trouble she has given.

No woman in a labor room should be too consciously the lady, or too nice to trouble her "team." Frankly, the staff is far more concerned with the job to be done than with her manners. The sounds of hard second-stage labor can be animal-like, and there is nothing in the delivery of a baby that can be called pretty. Anticipating that nice clean living and thinking and a brave spartan smile are going to do the job leads to disappointment for everyone. However, there are some advantages in natural childbirth for women emotionally and physically equipped to experience it. For example, an after-birth ecstacy nearly always appears after natural childbirth, and almost never after strong anesthesia.

Some women ask for "painless childbirth"—being put to sleep before or during second-stage labor and awakening after the baby is born. Thirty years ago this was the fad, but unfortunate results have discouraged the practice. The consequences of heavy sedation administered for this type of delivery can be grave: the mother may not cooperate to the extent necessary for a successful delivery, and the new-born sedated baby may suffer a delay in starting respiration.

Regardless of what "painless childbirth" means, it seems an unfortunate combination of words. Some women view one method or another of delivery as accomplishing "painless childbirth." Having their second, third, or fourth child, they may enjoy the experience tremendously, and exult about how wonderful, how painless it was, wishing they had used this method with their first child. But the easily delivered third is no assurance that the first would have been the same. The muscles have been strengthened and stretched to make later deliveries easier.

Thus far we have discussed only the normal pregnancy ending with one child, which is by far the most common. Multiple births, however, occur with some regularity as do a small number of complicated deliveries.

Multiple Births

Twins occur once in ninety births, triplets once in 8,000, and quadruplets once in 500,000. Multiple pregnancy may be due to the liberation of more than one egg from the ovaries in one menstrual cycle, or to the development of more than one individual from a single egg, or a combination of both. For example, it is possible to have quadruplets from one, two, three, or four eggs. All four could come from a division of one egg, two could come from each of two eggs, or two could come from one egg and two each from a separate egg, or all four could each come from a separate egg. Multiple babies from one egg are called *identical;* those carried in the uterus at the same time but born from different eggs are called *fraternal.* We will limit our discussion of multiple births to twins.

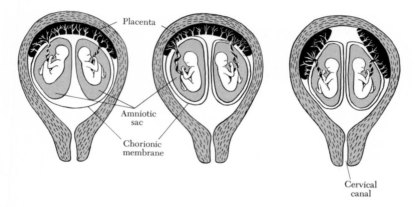

FIGURE 21.   *Fetal development of twins. Left: identical with one placenta, one chorionic membrane, two amniotic sacs. Center: fraternal with fused placenta, two chorionic membranes, two amniotic sacs. Right: fraternal with separate placentas, two chorionic membranes, two amniotic sacs.*

About two-thirds of all twins are fraternal and one-third are identical. Although the ovary generally produces one egg each menstrual cycle, ovulation can occur more than once. If it does and if two eggs are fertilized by two separate sperm cells, fraternal twins will be conceived. Since fraternal twins are the product of two entirely different eggs fertilized by two entirely different sperm cells, they are as unlike in heredity as any other two children of the same parents, and are not necessarily of the same sex.

Identical twins develop from one egg cell fertilized by one sperm cell. As a consequence they are identical in heredity and are always of the same sex. Neither the cause for the formation of two individuals from a single egg nor the way in which early development is altered to bring this about is definitely known. It is possible that shortly after the fertilized egg begins to develop, it splits in half. The timing of this split probably relates to how "identical" the twins are. If the separation takes place in the earliest embryonic stage, before cell differentiation, twins will probably be more alike than those resulting from a later split.

When twins are present in the uterus, each as a rule is attached to a placenta by its own umbilical cord. Fraternal twins implant independently in the uterine lining. If the sites are sufficiently far apart the placentas will be separate, and only the outer surfaces of the chorionic membranes will be in mutual contact. If the sites are close together the neighboring edges of the two placentas merge, two chorionic sacs develop and each embryo is surrounded by its own amniotic and chorionic membrane. Identical twins share the same placenta and chorionic sac, but each fetus has its own umbilical cord and, almost always, its own amniotic sac.

Because of exceptions to these implantation conditions, correlation tests are more direct evidence of whether twins are fraternal or identical. The individuals are compared by many characteristics thought to be influenced by heredity: sex, blood groups and types, blood pressure, pulse, respiration, eye color, vision, skin color, hair color and form, sole and hand patterns, height, weight, head shape, and facial details.

The determination is important because heredity and environment studies of twins would be confounded by assuming that persons had identical heredity when they did not, or vice versa. But the question might be asked whether twins are ever really identical. They cannot possibly have the same environment, even before birth. If their environments were always identical there would never be instances of one identical twin being born dead—and there are.

Joined twins are occasionally born from a single egg. Siamese twins are the most famous example. For such twins to be produced, the division of the inner cell mass must be not quite complete, and some portion must be shared by each embryo. This condition is called incomplete twinning. All but a few incomplete twins perish before birth.

Normal twinning seems to have some basis in heredity, apparent from the frequency of twins in some families. With identical twins, if a specific gene plays a part in causing the fertilized egg or embryo to split, it could be provided either by the egg or sperm cell, and thus by the mother or the father. The gene that produces fraternal twins, however, comes only from the mother since at least two eggs have to be matured at or about the same time.

The delivery of twins is, of course, more complicated than a single delivery. How much more complicated depends on how the two fetuses are situated in the uterus and their size and on whether they are near full term or premature at delivery. Few, if any, insurmountable problems exist, particularly when the alert obstetrician knows that twins are to be delivered. Twins are each smaller than single babies and, therefore, pose no special problems during pregnancy. However, successful gestation and delivery are greatly dependent on the mother's condition and the availability of good obstetrical care.

Unusual Deliveries

About 95 per cent of all deliveries are normal and uncomplicated. At times, however, breech deliveries and Cesarean sections are necessary.

In 96 per cent of all women ready to be delivered the baby lies in the uterus with its head in the mother's pelvic cavity and its buttocks up near her ribs. These cases are known as *vertex (head) presentations*. In other cases—about 3 per cent—the baby's buttocks lie in the mother's pelvis. These cases are known as *breech presentations*. Breech deliveries are more difficult for the mother and more hazardous for the baby. The use of forceps on the baby's head is common, but with caution and good obstetrical care the outcome is successful.

Other conditions also require instruments: a large head in a disproportionately small pelvis, evidence of fetal distress indicating the need for a quick delivery, a prolonged second stage of labor without satisfactory progress, or a fatigued uterus.

Today, instruments cause very little damage to mother or child. The ominous connotation of "instrument baby" no longer applies. Indeed, in many instances obstetricians use instruments almost rou-

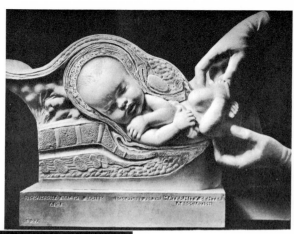

FIGURE 22. *Breech presentation.*

tinely to shorten the second stage of labor by assisting the delivery of the baby's head. They feel that unnecessary pounding against the pelvic floor to stretch and iron out those strong pelvic muscles is asking a lot of a baby's head. Although babies seem to recover quickly from the trauma of birth, authorities wonder what mild unrecognizable damage might be done to delicate brain cells under several hours of heavy second-stage labor. They would rather spare the head than let nature take its course unaided.

Heavy second-stage labor and a tight pelvis are not uncommon in a woman's first delivery. As she has other children, the pelvic structure is more relaxed and easier to dilate. A woman having her first baby, therefore, should be under the best obstetrical care possible.

Cesarean Section

Another obstetrical procedure that used to be far more hazardous than it is today is the Cesarean section, an operation in which the baby is delivered through an incision in the abdominal wall. The uterus is in turn incised, and delivery accomplished by one of several procedures devised to fit the individual situation. Antibiotics, blood banks, and improved anesthesia and surgical skill have reduced hazards, but it is still a major operation which carries some risk to the mother and should not be undertaken lightly. However, the operation may sometimes be necessary to save baby, mother, or both, or it may preclude some anticipated risk through normal delivery. Before performing a Cesarean section an obstetrician will usually confer with one or more colleagues to confirm that this type of delivery is indicated. Most hospitals require such a consultation.

Some conditions suggesting a Cesarean section are uterine hemorrhage in the last stages of pregnancy, disproportion of fetal head size to birth canal, certain illnesses or poor physical condition in the mother, trouble with organs (heart, kidneys, lungs) that might be burdened or harmed in the later stages of pregnancy or during prolonged and inefficient labor, or unexplained symptoms of fetal distress.

The relation of fetal head size to pelvic opening can be fairly well determined through examination by an experienced physician and by X-ray. Should there be any doubt, the patient is given a trial of labor and allowed to carry on if progress is satisfactory. If no satisfactory progress is made after about four to six hours of good labor, a Cesarean section is performed.

In good hands and good hospitals, fatalities to women having Cesareans are rare. Nevertheless the operation is approached with respect, and it is usual for a woman so delivered to have her next children in the same way, about ten to fourteen days before the expected date. In recent years some obstetrical centers have permitted women who have had Cesarean sections to be delivered normally in subsequent pregnancies, if conditions warrant. So far the results are positive, and this practice will probably increase. Women are cautioned to limit the number of Cesarean births to three, for the uterine scars grow weaker with each and there is always a chance of rupture of the uterus in the later stages of pregnancy. Be that as it may, some women have been delivered in this manner nine or more times, which proves only that they are truly hardy.

We shall now continue the discussion of an uncomplicated delivery.

adaptation and recovery (postnatal)

After delivery, mother and child need rest, for birth is exhausting. For the first twenty-four hours the baby is kept from the breast and given only sugar water. Within a few days the mother's milk appears, whether it is stimulated or not by the nursing of the baby. The initial secretion from the breast is a thin milk-like fluid (*colostrum*). It has a mildly laxative effect on the baby and helps to rid his intestinal tract of wastes which accumulated before he was born (*meconium*).

Hospitals with "rooming-in" allow the baby to stay in a cradle at the mother's bedside instead of in the nursery to get all the attention the mother wants to give him. She can start performing some of the functions she would not ordinarily take over until going home. Advocates of this practice feel that separating the mother and child after delivery may interfere with essential psychological needs of both, especially those of the baby.

Meanwhile, the mother is assured long hours of sleep, usually

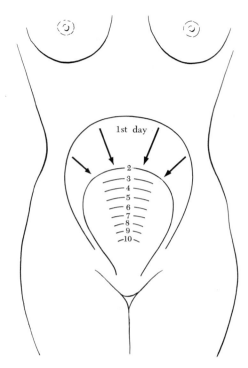

FIGURE 23.   *Postnatal shrinking of the uterus.*

with sedatives, as her uterus returns to normal. While shrinking, the uterus discharges a combination of blood, mucus, and semidissolved remnants of the lining of the uterus (*lochia*). At the start lochia is thick and bloody but gradually becomes paler and thinner. The discharge continues in diminishing amounts for two to five weeks on the average. During this period, especially for the first two or three days, the woman may be conscious of cramps (afterpains) especially after nursing that stimulate the uterus to empty itself. If these cramps are painful, or if the episiotomy wound is uncomfortable, the mother is given some mild medication.

During her stay at the hospital the mother may attend classes at which she learns about handling the baby, nursing, breast care, bathing, diapering, and most of the other things she will need to know to carry on when she is on her own at home. One of the more amusing aspects of baby care is the trepidation of new mothers and fathers in handling the new baby—they are so afraid of hurting, bruising, or dropping him. Fortunately, babies are not so fragile as they appear and all usually goes well in spite of apprehensions and clumsiness at the start.

Much has been written extolling the emotional satisfaction of a mother's relation to her new baby, most of it true and perhaps even understated. The satisfaction is also great for the husband who is now a *father* and feels more of a man. But with this great, unparalleled fulfillment there are prices to be paid.

Even with the best of care and exercise minor physical changes will have to be accepted. With or without nursing, the breasts will sag somewhat, although in a few women this is scarcely noticeable. The nipples will stay darkened. The abdominal wall will stretch, and unless carefully restrained by disciplined exercises, will remain soft and require a girdle (especially if the woman allowed herself to become overweight) to achieve a semblance of former shape. Silver stretch marks may show up on the abdomen and even on the hips and thighs. And then there might be varicosities (enlarged veins) in the legs, labia and elsewhere.

There are also emotional considerations. Women sometimes suffer a postnatal depression. They get over it, of course, but fathers should be prepared for a period in which the mother feels sorry for herself and has a diminished interest in him, the newborn, and the future—with some real anxiety about the future.

Probably the most important safeguard to a happy household with a newborn baby is a calm and unperturbed mother. There are doubtless many ways to work toward this end. At least three have been proved: avoiding too many visitors, cautioning against overwork, and having a helpful, considerate, and interested husband.

If this is a first child, the father should prepare himself for a loss in attention from the mother. Consciously or not, he may be jealous of the strong unity between mother and child. Tension can be eased if the mother admits him to the care of the child, encouraging him to help when he can. If the baby is bottlefed, he can certainly assist with this.

The return of menstruation varies. For women who do not nurse their babies, the flow returns four to six weeks after delivery. Those who breast-feed may not have a menstrual period until after the third month, and frequently later. In some cases, however, the menstrual period does not return until the baby is weaned. The first period is usually normal, but can be profuse, sometimes enough to cause alarm. If it is heavy, it is best for a woman to keep off her feet at that time.

The period of sexual continence continues for about six weeks after the birth of the baby, during the healing of the episiotomy, the shrinking of the uterus, and the return of the pelvic organs to their proper position and size. After that the couple can resume sexual intercourse. The recent mother may not be particularly receptive to intercourse; she usually has some early discomfort and may not experience orgasm until a considerable period after the birth of the child. Nor is the man so anxious to resume as the untutored might expect. Somehow he has a new healthy respect for the pelvic area as something more than just a means for sexual outlet. With time, however, sexual relations are resumed and are as satisfactory as they were before pregnancy, perhaps even more so now that there is a family to strengthen the ties and the love of the parents for each other.

Pregnancy Wastage

Now let us discuss the 20 to 25 per cent of pregnancies which do not go to term. The all-inclusive classification of pregnancies that end before the developing individual can live outside the mother is *pregnancy wastage*.

Termination of pregnancy during the first three months is called *abortion*, from the fourth through the sixth month, *miscarriage*, and from then until four weeks before the expected time of delivery, *premature birth*. Using *miscarriage* to describe an involuntary ending of pregnancy, and *abortion* to describe one that is artificially induced, are erroneous distinctions. To avoid confusion, some physicians now define abortion as all circumstances which put an end to pregnancy before the baby is sufficiently grown to survive by itself. A fetus should be at least twenty-eight weeks old to have a chance for survival. After thirty-two weeks chances are improved, but much special care is imperative.

Abortion has an unwholesome connotation. It is thought of primarily as the illegal removal of the embryo by surgery or other means. However, the word refers in fact to the detachment or expulsion of the embyro from the uterus whatever the means or reason. If the separation is unintentional, the abortion is termed *spontaneous*. If the embryo is deliberately removed by surgery or other means, abortion is said to be *induced*.

Spontaneous abortions may be classified into those resulting from random or fortuitous factors, sometimes known but mostly unknown and unlikely to recur in another pregnancy—the larger category—and those in which a persistent factor appears with succeeding pregnancies. The latter are known as *habitual abortions*.

There are many possible causes of spontaneous abortion. For example, defects may exist in the sperm, egg cell, developing embryo, or in the structure or condition of the uterus. Hormonal imbalance in the early stages of implantation may also be responsible.

About 70 per cent of the spontaneous abortions occur during the second and third month of pregnancy. Typically, pregnancy does in fact commence and a menstrual period is missed. The woman, however, may notice some tendency to cramps or slight vaginal staining. This may subside with bed rest after a few days, or it may become more pronounced with slight-to-moderate bleeding. At this stage the condition is known as *threatened abortion*. It is still difficult to determine whether the threat to the pregnancy will subside or whether an abortion will occur. All measures to preserve the pregnancy are employed: bed rest, abstinence from sexual intercourse, treatment with hormone medication, and sedation. Sometimes the results are good and the pregnancy continues, but sometimes the efforts are of no avail.

If the condition progresses to heavy bleeding and severe cramps it is called *inevitable abortion,* and the woman goes on to expel the products of conception. If they are entirely expelled this is known as *complete spontaneous abortion*. Sometimes the embryo is seen, sometimes not. But if the products of conception remain in the uterus and the woman continues to bleed and have contractions the condition is called *incomplete spontaneous abortion*. These cases usually require hospitalization so that the remnants can be surgically removed from the uterus (scraping or curettage). The clean uterus returns more quickly to the normal state, free of impediments to future pregnancies. Occasionally a condition is seen where the embryo dies but is retained in the uterus for several weeks before it is passed. This condition is known as a *missed abortion* and usually requires curettage.

Other causes of spontaneous abortion may include glandular imbalance, nutritional deficiencies, and the toxic effect of diseases and drugs on the embryo. Physical trauma—injury, falling, frequent and vigorous intercourse, long and jarring automobile rides —may also be at fault, but apparently only when the embryo has not been implanted properly. But with the present state of obstetrical knowledge, most causes have to be determined more from conjecture than fact, and it is often difficult to separate cause from coincidence. This is particularly true of spontaneous miscarriages yielding in the fourth or fifth month a perfectly normal-looking fetus which is simply not living.

Progress is being made in the treatment of some causes of spontaneous abortion. Cases of hormonal imbalance, for example, can sometimes be remedied by judicious treatment with hormone medications.

Induced abortions are either *therapeutic,* or more often, *illegal.* Therapeutic abortion is a legal termination of pregnancy by artificial means. Such abortions can be performed only if two qualified physicians testify that continuation of the pregnancy would jeopardize the life or health of the mother. Inherited conditions such as susceptibility to uncontrolled bleeding in males (*hemophilia*), or certain forms of idiocy may also be accepted occasionally as reasons for therapeutic abortion. But eugenic, medical, and psychiatric indications are not standardized, and the same set of conditions may be accepted by one group of physicians and rejected by another, or may be legal reasons in one state and illegal in another.

Therapeutic abortion may not be performed in the United States simply because a woman wishes it, or because of economic or social factors, although there is increasing consideration of her mental health. In certain borderline cases, however, the patient's prestige or money may be influential in ending an undesired pregnancy. To reduce pressures of personal influence and to ensure a thoroughly considered decision, leading hospitals have set up abortion committees to review all requests for abortion—private and ward.

Therapeutic abortion is carried out as a vaginal operation if the pregnancy has lasted fewer than twelve to thirteen weeks. It is usually performed before but near the eighth week, at which time it is technically easier and less hazardous. The cervix of the uterus is dilated with instruments and the products of conception removed. If the pregnancy goes beyond thirteen weeks, the uterus is generally emptied by abdominal and uterine incision.

Illegal abortion presents one of the most serious yet least studied questions of modern medicine. Society is aware of the problem, suppresses it, and as far as possible ignores it. By estimate, well over one million illegal abortions are carried out each year in the United States. The vast majority—perhaps 75 per cent —are performed on married women, particularly those experiencing third or fourth pregnancies they do not wish or cannot afford. About 50 per cent are performed by physicians, 20 per cent by midwives, and 30 per cent by the women themselves, sometimes with the help of the man associated. The last two groups account for most of the tragic physical complications.

The dangers of illegal abortion are emotional and physical. Because of the clandestine nature of the operation and the people implicated, it is likely to be degrading for the woman, an experience slowly, if ever, forgotten. While the woman usually experiences relief at escaping from the immediate problem of an unwanted pregnancy, she frequently suffers depression due to conscious and unconscious guilt feelings. Some of the love the woman has for the man who made her pregnant is destroyed. She feels that she has killed her child, and therefore a part of herself. She feels devaluated, worthless, inferior. She also fears that she may have harmed her reproductive organs permanently. The sense of remorse deepens as she wonders if she can conceive again. Later, if she actually experiences difficulty conceiving, the remorse is intensified. Even after becoming pregnant she may feel compelled to tell her physician about her abortion for fear that something wrong with her may adversely influence the pregnancy.

The physical dangers of illegal abortion are hemorrhage and infection; the latter may end in sealed Fallopian tubes and sterility. If the uterus is perforated, the threat to life can be serious. Fortunately the rates of infection and death have been cut drastically by antibiotics; nevertheless things still go wrong when desperate women turn to brutal surgery and then fail to see their own physicians for a checkup.

Now and then the law organizes against illegal abortionists, and there is a temporary suppression; but like a nasty boil, the situation suppressed in one area will erupt close by. Eventually society will grow up to its responsibilities and find a solution to this matter. But that may be a long way off because the law frequently equates human sexual and reproductive needs with evil and treats them accordingly. Like so many other troublesome problems that society has not had the courage to tackle, this one has been thrown in the lap of the medical profession, with sufficient legal restriction to prevent any sensible solution.

Medical abortionists are a strange breed of professional men, living outside the pale of professional respectability, working for the money, and hoping to escape detection until they can retire or switch to legitimate practice. Some few, however, seem to be dedicated men who through a desire to make the best of a bad situation have decided to help women caught by circumstance.

When a woman feels she needs the help of an abortionist she usually goes to her family physician. He can try to determine whether she is actually pregnant. She may only be suffering a missed or delayed menstrual period. (About 10 per cent of illegal abortions are performed by unscrupulous abortionists on women who are not pregnant.) He rarely can do anything beyond the determination of pregnancy. His own hands are tied, and it is likely that he does not know an abortionist even if he wishes to recommend one. The woman finds her answer through young married women who had a similar problem, or who know of someone else who did. They pass the name along.

The unwed mother is a special case. When young, unmarried, pregnant women come into a physician's office, they often admit that they have not confided in their parents. Most of them are shocked even to think of doing this because it is their parents that they fear the most. Most parents *want* their children to come to them for help in time of trouble. Certainly they will be shocked, hurt, and unhappy, but their children are unrealistic if they think that parents have not lived through the heartaches and problems of growing up. On the other hand, parents can try to impress upon their children not only the necessity of attaining a sense of maturity and responsibility, but also the assurance that they may turn to them for support and guidance in time of trouble.

The most dangerous variety of illegal abortion is performed

by the woman on herself. All kinds of implements are used: hat pins, hair pins, slippery elm sticks. Piercing the uterus with such instruments, and resultant infections, have caused some tragic deaths—all the more so because sometimes the victim was not even pregnant.

Pills and drugs to abort a pregnancy are sold by the carload and are useless, in spite of the protestations of women who "know" that they work. They can be swallowed to the point of self-poisoning without other effect. The "black pill" sought at drug stores is just a form of ergot or quinine, drugs that, it is hoped, will stimulate uterine contractions. One possible explanation for what seems like occasional success with one of these techniques is that the emotional and psychological strain of the rejection of the pregnancy contributes to a spontaneous abortion. But most of the time coincidence is at work, and the women who have, soon after taking the pill, the delayed menstrual period or spontaneous abortion they were going to have anyway, are numerous enough to keep the market going. Hot douches, strong purgatives, high diving, bouncing downstairs, and parachute jumping are equally ineffective.

At present, there is no satisfactory solution to the abortion dilemma. Homes for unmarried mothers reduce the problem somewhat. Enlightened administration of these can provide not only a place for the unwed mother to receive good obstetrical care, but a chance for her to explore the advantages and disadvantages of keeping her child or of giving it up for adoption. In addition, special programs while she is in residence can acquaint her with preventive techniques and otherwise attempt to help her to develop a responsible code of sexual conduct. But the majority of abortions are performed on married women who were made pregnant by their husbands. For them part of the answer is a better understanding of preventive techniques. Alternate schemes, such as improved adoption facilities for the children of married couples who do not wish them and liberalized abortion laws, seem, in the main, to treat the symptoms rather than the cause of this social malady.

psychosexual development

THE EMOTION OF LOVE and the sexual impulse do not appear suddenly in adolescence. Along with personality, their development begins at birth and continues throughout life. Personality, character, emotions, sexuality, attitudes, opinions, what we are, and what we would like to be, begin to be formed from the moment we are born. But even at that early moment there are already within us characteristics which influence our capacities and limits.

Genetic Inheritance

First there is our genetic inheritance decided at the moment of conception. Heredity influences appearance, size, intellectual ability. Children are also born with different degrees of muscular response and this may be an early influence on their physical activities—how soon they crawl, walk, play ball, and perhaps whether they become gifted athletes. Soon after birth, one child will be more social or even-tempered than another. Finally, the sex of the child will have a marked influence on the way it lives its life. Newborn infants, then, already have certain genetically determined predispositions.

Environment

But the shaping of an individual from birth to adulthood, what he becomes, and the extent to which he achieves his inherited potential, will depend largely on the environment in which he is reared. For the infant, environment is primarily the physical, emotional, and psychological conditions provided by the parents, particularly the mother. For the first years of life, the child is rooted and contained in the family constellation. His place in the family, that is, whether he is the first or only child, how many brothers and sisters he has, will influence his later ability to form relations with other people. The handling and discipline he receives, the attitudes conveyed by a look, a tone of voice, or by praise or punishment, will influence his reaction to persons in authority. His response to them may affect his own adult role in relation to authority. At one extreme he may show a tendency to become too submissive, at the other, too domineering. The training he receives in such matters as manners and cleanliness, and the age at which it occurs, might later make him rigid and compulsive about high standards of personal cleanliness or, by reaction formation, slovenly.

The child's sense of security will reflect the type of care his parents, particularly the mother, provide. Relaxed handling, tenderness, warmth, will give him a sense of well-being and acceptance, and he will have a good foundation for developing into a self-confident adult. If his parents are abrupt, tense, irritated, or impatient with him, he will feel relatively insecure, and this may lead in turn to doubts and inability to trust others. The way parents feel about the sex of the child, whether they are happy or unhappy with a boy or a girl, and their expressed or implied attitudes about this, will have an effect upon the child's own feelings later on about being a man or woman. As the child grows older he is increasingly exposed to experiences outside of the family—e.g., association with peers, mores of community, church, and school—which will exert their influence on the sort of adult he becomes.

Genetic inheritance and environmental factors together bear upon psychosexual development. Sex and love develop within us from birth, but the bodily centers of gratification change as the individual matures. According to the Freudian concept, nature's timetable for psychosexual development is organized into five phases: oral, anal, genital, latent, and adolescent. During these phases we develop the emotions of love, our attitudes toward sex itself, and our feelings about the opposite sex. These factors contribute to the kind of person we are for the rest of our lives.

oral phase

For the first year of a child's life gratification centers on his mouth. He derives pleasure from sucking. As tensions due to hunger mount he responds with crying and searches with his mouth. As he nurses or feeds from the bottle, his sucking and hunger tensions are relieved, and he thus experiences his first pleasurable sensations. The mouth is therefore termed the first erotic zone.

Many satisfying emotions we have in adulthood date back to these first pleasurable experiences. The part which the lips and mouth play in nursing are related later on to the pleasure derived from such activities as eating, drinking, kissing, and smoking.

In the first months of life, the infant already needs more than a physiologically adequate environment. While the uncomfortable sensation of hunger is being relieved, a different kind of hunger is also being satisfied—his very strong need for closeness to the mother. He needs to be fondled, cuddled, to be held close to his mother, to be given an undisturbed period for nursing or feeding and adequate sucking. The satisfaction of cuddling against the mother, particularly as his cheek is pressed against her breast and his body against her body, may help to build up a feeling of pleasure associated with stroking the skin or holding the body of a loved one later in life. After the first six months, when teeth begin to appear, the infant starts to bite as well as suck. Biting is pleasurable because it relieves the soreness of the gums and he derives the same type of pleasure from it as he previously obtained from sucking. He is using his mouth as a medium for both love and hostility. This is the first evidence of ambivalence—the ability to love and hurt the same person. Through such emotional contacts a loving mother will give the child a feeling of security and well-being. If to this picture is added a father who supports the mother in the way she handles the child, and who himself handles him with warmth and enjoys having him around, the child is highly likely to negotiate the oral phase successfully. If, however, the child spends the first few months of his life in an atmosphere in which these essentials are lacking, his emotional growth will be impaired, and this may be difficult to remedy subsequently. He may make burdensome demands of loved ones later on to make up for deprivations during the oral phase. He may wish to be sheltered and pampered, to have someone close at hand to provide for his needs as convincing proof of their love.

As these factors in psychosexual development are described, some readers might feel that even a single isolated lapse in properly serving the needs of the child will have lasting harmful effects. *All* parents are at times short tempered, irritable, and less-than-loving toward their children and each other. It is the over-all pattern of parental conduct that is important. An occasional lapse is to be expected, and perfection is neither possible nor desirable. A lack of perfection may even help children to become less rigid, more tolerant, flexible, and adjustable human beings.

anal phase

The anal phase overlaps the oral phase somewhat and runs from the end of the first year to about the end of the third year. Some time after the first year the nerves activating the anal sphincter develop to a point where the infant can begin to exert some control over defecation. The child has an interest in this new power of being able to either evacuate or retain his feces, and takes some pleasure in his bowel movement. His major source of gratification shifts from the mouth to the anus, making it the second erotic zone.

At about this time his mother becomes interested in toilet training him, and both the interests of the child and mother are now focused on his bowel movement. In our culture, toilet training has to be accomplished as hygienically as possible, and we have to teach our children that feces are "dirty," to be deposited at a particular place and usually at a particular time, when he is put on the "potty." But the attitude of the child toward his feces is entirely different from that of an adult—the first major conflict between the child and his environment.

The fact that his feces are of his own creation and the product of a new physical achievement makes him value them very much. He has none of the disgust about them which adults have. He admires, and would like to keep them. He is at a loss to know why something he values so much is of so little importance to his mother. Even when he gives the feces to her at the time she wishes, she discards them, calls them "a mess" and warns him not to touch them, that they are dirty. He is beset by confusion which he resolves in one of several ways. He can rebel against his mother's wishes and retain his bowel movement. He will of course have to defecate eventually—but in the time and place *he* chooses. This will of course expose him to his mother's displeasure. Or he may also begin thinking his feces are "bad," as his parents do, and he can expel them in some *hidden* place; and the soiling that results from this expresses his hostility at having to think his feces are bad.

But because of his complete dependence on his parents, and in order to retain their approval and love, he eventually submits more or less grudgingly to toilet training. He gives up his feelings about his feces and finds substitute expression in more socially acceptable ways; playing with dough, clay, sand, mud, water, finger paints. He might come to value some other possession highly, like *his* toys.

Considering how important these matters are to the child, the way in which the mother handles toilet training can be of lasting consequence. Depending on how much a child is forced in toilet training he may become submissive or rebellious later on. If in the battle of wills, the mother is relaxed and tolerant about toilet training and neither takes a strong stand nor forces the child into one, he is usually relaxed and tolerant too, and ultimately accomplishes the training satisfactorily. If she emphasizes how *dirty* and *disgusting* it is, he may begin to feel that way too, and later on all kinds of dirtiness and disorder may become repulsive to him. Throughout his life he may be overclean and meticulous about details and order, leaving himself little room for spontaneity and adventure. While these character traits are not fully developed in this early stage, the seeds are sown.

During the oral and anal phases of psychosexual development, a good part of the infant's interest is directed to himself. He is concerned with the enjoyment of his own needs and sensations and likes others to serve him. This seems perfectly acceptable conduct for the infant. Unfortunately some "infants" continue at this stage for thirty, forty or more years, making demands on a love relationship that can be troublesome to those about them, or destructive. We have all met the adult who measures other people by how much they do for him, how much he can get out of them, how much they can help him to enjoy his own sensations.

genital or oedipal phase

As strong emotions about defecation subside there is a heightened awareness of feelings in the genitals; this introduces the genital phase which runs from the third to the sixth year. The child learns that pressure from a full bladder or from clothing, or feeling the genitals with his fingers gives a pleasant sensation. Although the pleasurable feelings were present earlier, they now come to the fore. Interest centers in the genital organs themselves —penis for the boy, clitoris for the girl—and in the handling and stimulation of them. Thus the genitals become the third erotic zone.

At the same time, the child becomes curious about other people's genital areas, and begins to notice sex differences. Until they become aware of differences in the genitals, the psychosexual development of boy and girl do not differ much. This awareness opens separate roads for them, which according to Freudian concepts take specific paths largely trodden in the "unconscious."

For the boy, tensions of the genital phase come primarily from intensified love feelings for his mother. He begins to compete with his father for the love and attention of his mother. He takes this "romance" quite seriously, and many little boys say to their mothers, "When I grow up, I am going to marry you." This rivalry with the father for the mother's affection is called the *oedipal complex*, after the protagonist in Sophocles' tragedy *Oedipus Rex* who unknowingly was destined to kill his father and marry his mother. The little boy, while continuing to love and admire his father, wishes to replace him in his mother's affection. This wish to replace him means, in effect, wishing him out of the way, and the boy feels guilty.

In addition he fears his father's retaliation, which he believes will take the form of castration. Curiously enough, such a threat need never have been made or implied for a boy to fear castration. By this time he is aware that there are human beings who do not possess a penis, and it is easy to conclude that it can be lost or taken away. He values his penis highly, as an area of pleasurable sensation and as a means of identification with his father—a pass-key to masculinity and, eventually, adult sexuality. In addition, without it, how could he successfully compete with his father?

Rather than continue to run the phantasied risk of castration, the boy during the late genital phase begins to renounce his erotic strivings toward his mother and takes himself out of competition with his father. Guilt over his erotic strivings toward his mother and over his hostile feelings toward his father, plus his need to identify with his father in order to have before him an image of the masculine person he wishes to grow up to be, combine to help him to emerge from the genital phase.

For the girl, as mentioned earlier, erotic feelings during this phase center in the clitoris. She finds both pleasure, and a means for dealing with tensions in the stroking and manipulation of this organ. In the early stages of this phase, her affections continue to be directed toward her mother. However, as she starts comparing her genitals to those of the male she discovers that he has a penis and she does not. She envies the boy his penis, and blames her mother who has hitherto provided her with everything, for failing to provide her with this. She feels disappointed, cheated, and alienated from her mother. Her affection and phantasies shift to the father. At first these involve being given a penis by him, then progress to being given a baby by him. And as the boy became a competitor of his father, the little girl becomes her mother's rival.

Parents have to be tolerant of the family "romances" and the hostilities and jealousies expressed by the children. Eventually the children realize the impracticality of courting their parents. The boy directs his efforts toward emulating his father's masculinity. His erotic strivings toward his mother are repressed and he now expresses tenderness and affection toward her. The girl overcomes much of her hostility toward her mother and erotic strivings toward her father. This differentiation into masculinity and femininity is the important maturation taking place in the genital period. When the boy comes to identify with his father and to emulate him, he is signifying his acceptance of the active, aggressive, masculine role. When the wish to be given a penis by the father is replaced in the girl by a wish to be given a baby, this is the beginning of her acceptance of the passive, receptive role. These roles are the definition of masculinity and femininity in our culture in so far as sexuality is concerned.

For most the genital period is negotiated satisfactorily, but some fail to end the dependencies of the family romance. For them sexual love never gets beyond being a "mommy's boy" or a "daddy's girl." Another symptom of failure is equating genital feelings with the whole of love. Such feelings are an inseparable part of the adult love life, but they are certainly not the main or only part.

While having started on the road toward adult sexuality, however, the child's phantasies about the nature of sexual relations are still distorted. His concept of the relationship between the sexes can be only what he has experienced in his own life, for he is still at the stage where he believes that people are what he is, think the way he thinks, feel what he feels, and do what he does. He has knowledge of sucking, biting, and eating from the oral phase; urinating and defecating from the anal phase; and touching, fondling, manipulating, and so forth from the genital phase. Because he does not yet have the capacity for abstract thinking or imagination at his disposal, the child between three and six years has his own distorted view of sexual relations, and even if he is told differently at this age, he is not able to understand.

A word about masturbation during this phase seems in order here. Unfortunately, on occasion, concern over castration is heightened when a parent tries to discourage a child from masturbating by threatening to "cut off" his genitals. Also, children do show new interest in their genitals during this phase, and parents are sometimes troubled and want to know what to do about it. They are apt to think of masturbation as sinful or undesirable despite the lip service currently paid to the idea that it is a natural and normal activity in sexual development. The fact is, though, that touching the genitals in infancy and masturbatory activity in older children *is usual and normal.*

Many young parents know this intellectually, not emotionally. It is necessary to overcome one's own shame and embarrassment about masturbation in order to allow one's children to develop

naturally and healthfully. When adults see a child touch his
genitals they view it in the framework of adult sexuality; but the
child's interest is purely physical and just as natural as satisfying
any other physical need. By bringing gratification through the
genitals, masturbation plays a positive role in the sexual maturation
of the individual. Of course, after a certain age a child should not
touch his genitals in public, but this can be explained to him in
a way that he understands: masturbation is as natural as urination
and defecation, but no more to be carried on in public than are
these activities. To tell a child that masturbation is something
which is done in private, like going to the toilet, is necessary and
sensible; to forbid it on the basis that it is harmful or evil is unfortunate; at best it may give him the feeling that sex is something
bad and so are his genitals, and thereby run the risk of delaying
or impeding his adult sexuality. The concentration of erotic
gratification in the genitals is desirable in all respects (in view
of their role in propagation), and nothing should be done to interfere. The suppression of gratification may lay the groundwork for
sexual maladjustment in adult life resulting in conditions such as
frigidity or impotence.

To condone masturbation is not the same as encouraging it.
A child who is allowed to masturbate does not do so any more
frequently than the one who has been forbidden to. Condoning
it is treating the matter realistically and directly. Forbidding it is
simply creating anxieties and fears about something the child will
probably continue to do anyway.

latent phase

After the genital phase, the child's emotional involvement in
erotic gratification tends to subside temporarily. Between the ages
of six and ten he experiences the latent phase of his psychosexual
development. His curiosity about sexual matters continues, but
is pursued with less vigor and feeling. Sex becomes more of a group
game at this age involving some exhibition of genitals and perhaps some genital play. Sexual love is not directed toward one
object (a parent) as it was in the genital phase, or as it will be
(a sweetheart) in the adolescent phase. He does not progress so

much in sexual development as he stabilizes; he does not change so much as he becomes more of what he already is.

However, it is a time of widening horizons elsewhere. The importance of his family and his dependence on them recede somewhat as much of his time and attention is given to friends. Their opinions begin to matter. Whereas it used to be, "My mother says . . ." and "My father says . . . ," now it is, "Harry says. . . ." He also begins to think more for himself, to have ideas of his own. His intellectual capacity grows, and he learns to cope with the everyday problems he used to turn over to his parents.

It is well that children start school at the age of six, for as the strength of the erotic drive subsides, energy is freed for learning. A child's mental development encourages a keen interest in facts—sexual facts included. He begins to compare his parents' answers with those of teachers and friends. It is especially important that parents give truthful, straightforward answers to his questions during this period, for on this basis his confidence in them may be built or undermined. Their role in his life as an adolescent may possibly be determined here.

Children at this stage play endlessly with their friends. They invent games, make up stories, and begin to find access to the world of phantasy and imagination. As physical coordination increases, they begin to enjoy games of skill and enter happily into competition. They develop feelings of understanding and empathy with their friends. They learn to love altruistically, not just for self-satisfaction. Relying less on parents, they at the same time become less individualistic and more conforming with friends. They want to be accepted by their friends; they wear similar clothes and share in the same pursuits and pleasures. There is a feeling of a strength in numbers.

Most of their friends are of the same sex. During this phase the sexes are not particularly concerned with each other; there may even be a little mild hostility. Boys and girls tease each other but do not chum around together conspicuously. They feel more at ease with their own sex, where the demands are more physical than emotional.

Some parents resent the decline in their influence and attempt to impose their will and thus inhibit the striving of the child for growth outside the family. If they are forceful enough and tie their tactics in with a child's sense of security, they may succeed. Other parents are somewhat disturbed by a child's lack of interest in the opposite sex and try to stimulate it a little. They tease about the boy in school, or the girl next door. Pushing this way can actually delay a child's interest. He may find some experiences unpleasant because he is unready for them, and thus be discouraged from entering into them when he should be ready. If parents are patient, the hormones will become increasingly active, bringing development to the point where matters can take care of themselves. On the other hand there are parents so relieved by the relative absence of sexual symptoms in their child during this phase—and the easing of their own tensions and worry about such symptoms—that they want to keep things that way. They reinforce the idea of "good boy" and "good girl" so successfully that the child loses interest in sex to conform to the wishes of his parents. He may delay picking this interest up again in adolescence.

In the usual course of events, however, by the time the child is approaching ten, most parents are ready to congratulate themselves. They note how much the child has grown physically, how teachable he is, how reasonable, friendly, and understanding he seems to have become. They feel he has turned out well indeed, and that some praise may be in order for the job they have done. And then comes adolescence.

adolescent phase

Adolescence is that period between the tenth and eighteenth years. For convenience of description, it will be divided into preadolescence (ages ten to twelve), early adolescence (twelve to fourteen), and late adolescence (fourteen to eighteen). There is of course some overlap in these periods and variation in timing from child to child.

Preadolescence

During the latent phase of development what took place was a kind of firming of the whole person, an emotional stabilization of all the results of psychosexual phases that had gone before, accompanied by physical, social, and intellectual growth. Physical sexual development was slower and strong emotions about sex temporarily subsided. But in the preadolescent phase hormones accelerate sexual maturation and trigger sexual drives. The child who in latency seemed so settled now begins to show signs of instability. He is overcome by the strangeness of these new and powerful sexual feelings and does not yet know how to handle them or give them proper expression.

At this stage, the girl is ahead of the boy in physical development. She is often taller, stronger, and more physically mature, and the boy may feel inferior. This is one reason why boys tend to run in gangs at this age and to show little interest in girls. In contrast, probably because of their more advanced biological development, girls are much more interested in boys. Their chasing after boys, though, is more of a socially fostered cultural rite than the mature wish of a woman for a man. There is avid sexual curiosity but no desire for sexual intercourse as yet and no great amount of emotion is involved.

During the preadolescent phase some idealization of the same sex occurs. Close friendships and shared secrets are characteristic. Among both sexes erotic feelings are apt to be directed to members of the same sex, but among boys in particular this may give rise to some sexual acts, such as mutual masturbation or even group masturbation or exhibition of sexual organs. In the main, however, these homosexual episodes do not influence or retard heterosexual development.

A child may enter preadolescence with an emerging confidence in his ability to reach his own decisions. Parents should encourage this confidence by guiding him to good decisions when he needs help, not by forcing him to reach decisions he does not feel equipped to make. Eventually the child will be an adult who should be able to make up his own mind about matters. The more practice he has, the better.

There is obviously a transition period during which he needs *practice* and *advice*. He will be more likely to listen to a parent whose judgment he trusts. The ability to plan for the future and to postpone the gratification of immediate wants in order to achieve long-range objectives is more easily developed if, from infancy, the individual has been able to rely on and trust people in the world in which he lives. The parent will have to state clearly what it is he expects the child to do or believe in. The child will raise questions. The parent's answers and arguments will have to stand on their merits; they will no longer be accepted simply because he said them or because they were accompanied with a show of authority. This challenge to parental authority may anger and disturb the parent.

Standards can be imposed by parents for only a limited time with limited success. Ultimately the decision to honor those standards must come from the child. If he understands the reason for them, he is more likely to honor them. It also helps a child to good decisions if he sees the parent living up to the standards and values advocated. A living example is a far greater force than an encyclopedia of advice. Unfortunately, a number of the standards imposed and decisions reached during adolescence are "sex loaded," and this reduces the influence of reason—on the part of both parent and child. A solution will be satisfactory only to the extent that reason remains in force.

Parents and other moral guardians are usually conservative in their sex values, probably because they have passed the peak of sexual desire and have acquired a sense of perspective about it. The early adolescent, however, is just at that point where sexual drives are urgent—and this separates them by a wide and deep gulf. Adolescence is the age of resentment against parental restriction. This will be even more pronounced in late adolescence. If sex is the area in which parents are most restrictive, it is likely to be the area in which there will be the greatest rebellion.

Early Adolescence

Between the ages of twelve and fourteen biological maturation is accelerated as evidenced by the appearance of secondary sex characteristics. The girl begins to menstruate, her breasts develop, her pubic hair grows, and her body takes on a womanly look in general. The boy's voice deepens, and his beard begins to grow. The penis and testes become larger and heavier and a source of concern or pride, depending on their size. He experiences sexual dreams which result in ejaculation ("wet dreams"), and masturbation with ejaculation is now possible.

But psychological growth does not keep pace with this rapid biological maturation. This is really the core of the adolescent problem. Physical growth outstrips emotional growth. The adolescent is bigger "outside" than "inside." He spends more of his time with his peers, becoming more aware of himself as a being in society, rather than as simply one member of a family. He tries to achieve an independent, secretive life of his own, but has spurts of almost total dependence on his family.

Whereas before it was only the girl who was interested in the opposite sex, now the boy begins to share this interest. He becomes concerned about his appearance, and is apt to bathe more frequently without being told, and to dress more neatly with greater attention to what he is wearing. A generalized interest in the other sex appears. A boy is interested in almost any girl, and a girl in almost any boy. They start dating, and seek superficial erotic gratification in early love play. Investments of love in the other sex have yet to be learned. They are trying to find out what the opposite sex is like and how they rate in relation to it.

In this search for a role, adolescents look about them for behavior models. They observe the way in which their parents treat each other, and their standards of conduct with members of the opposite sex. They also observe the behavior of other adults in person and in television, movies, newspapers, etc. These observations help to form a concept of self, including phantasies that tell them how to treat or be treated by the opposite sex.

Sexual curiosities, desires, and anxieties become more intense during early adolescence. In part this is due to the increased activity of the hormones, which in turn gives rise to sexual tension. It is also due to a strong psychological drive to grow up quickly— as if the mind and emotions were trying to catch up with the body —and to make "sex" symbolic of this growth. The tension created cannot yet be released in relation to another person, and masturbation is resorted to; now, however, it is not the simple type of manipulation of the genitals which occurred at an earlier age, but is accompanied by sexual phantasy.

The feeling of fondness and affection appears in intensified form, unassociated with any particular part of the body. The baby had learned to be fond of his mother and others in a general way, without having the feeling localized anywhere. The feeling is reawakened in early adolescence, and focused on selected members of the opposite sex.

A circulatory phenomenon called *thrill* appears. It is marked by quick breathing, pounding heart, a generalized tension and excitement that, once experienced, will not soon be forgotten. It is what young people think of as being in love. Under the stimulus of these feelings, discriminative selection in boy-girl relations tends to increase year by year. First boys and girls go around in groups. Eventually they pair off on individual dates and may "go steady."

Aroused sexual feelings, apprehension about masturbation and menstruation, loosening ties to the family, the emerging personality of the adolescent, the admonishments of parents who wish to be sure that no sex-related tragedies befall their children—all combine to create anxiety. Nonetheless, there are many happy and bittersweet sexual and romantic experiences during this phase which contribute positively to psychosexual maturity. Young love can yield sensitive and rewarding moments, the value and seriousness of which are traditionally underestimated by adults.

Late Adolescence

With the advance of adolescence, there is a final turn toward heterosexuality, renunciation of the incestuous love objects of the family romance, and a repression of homosexual love objects. The sexual drives become so strong and the outlets such as masturbation so inadequate that sublimation is utilized. Adolescents begin to look for substitute outlets in intellectual, philosophical, and religious experiences, and through creative arts and sports. Sublimation not only uses the energies of the sex drive, but can channel them into the achievement of one's goals. Here the parents and community can be helpful by providing adequate intellectual and recreational experiences.

Late adolescents begin to pull away from the family, forming an independent philosophy, character, and social awareness. The decline of parental influence is accelerated. The response of the family to his actions may no longer be as significant to the adolescent as what his girl friend, or an associate, or he himself thinks.

By this time he should have some internal bases for his decisions about sexual behavior. Confidence in his own behavior as an alternate to the standards of his peers is more easily formed now if during childhood he was exposed to exemplary behavior from which standards could be derived and if he was encouraged to exercise initiative. His experiences should have provided a freedom to fail sometimes, to experiment with many roles in the process of exploring his skills and abilities. If he has had no such experiences, his normal adolescent indecision about matters, including sexual behavior, will be compounded.

But his behavior is no straight line progression. One day the adolescent will behave like a reasonable adult and his parents will heave a sigh of relief. But the next day he will be childish and silly. His parents wonder whether he will ever grow up.

He is a creature of fluctuating moods and concerns, frequently straining the patience of the people about him. One day he will be gregarious and spend every moment with his friends; the next he will hardly say hello but go straight to his room and lock himself in. One day she will leave a trail of belongings strewn through the house; the next she may clean the house more thoroughly than her mother can, and then scold her for not being a better housekeeper. One day he will be totally independent and rebellious; the next he will be cooperative and pleasant. One day he will have the energy of three people; the next he will lie all day on his bed. In some cases the fluctuation will extend to his studies, his choice of vocation, his girl friends, and to his own worth and future hopes.

As the boy and girl approach the end of adolescence they must cope with sexual activities over which they have no control, such as sexual dreams, nocturnal emissions, and menstruation; and those over which they have control, such as masturbation, petting, and intercourse. And suddenly the unpleasant consequences of some of their activities can be much more serious. Whereas disciplinary breaches up to this point may have resulted in a slap or a disapproving look, easily absorbed and understood by youngsters, such breaches can now result in pregnancy or venereal disease and accompanying problems of such magnitude that the young people have no way to cope with them. There is also society's pressure for them to become men and women so they can marry and have children; fortunately most of them eventually do just that.

But some never leave adolescence. The opposite sex is attractive to them, but responsibility in reference to anyone in particu-

lar is avoided. They do not have the strength of personal security
to carry such responsibilities. A few may in time develop the necessary emotional strength to make good later marriages.

The phases of sexual development are universal, but the
success with which they are negotiated is a highly individual
matter. If a need is frustrated excessively, growth during that
phase may be thwarted or arrested and more characteristics or
needs of that phase retained than is normal, making one less likely
to grow in his next stage. In short, by the time a person has reached
the age at which he makes decisions about sexual practices and
love feelings, a lot has happened to him which will influence his
needs and expectancies from sex and love. The decisions he makes
will in part be based on those needs and expectancies. Also influencing his decisions will be the sex education he has acquired
and something of the attitudes about sex which he finds in his
segment of society.

sex education

Whether children should receive sex education is no longer
an issue. The practical question is one of when, how, and through
whom. Here the parents are in a strategic position, for it is in the
home that the child gets his first ideas and values about life—
including sex. A small child's sex education begins no later than
the discovery of his genitals. His mother's response to his handling
of them, the expression on her face, and her gestures tell him more
than her words.

Some parents are ideally equipped by training and personal
experience to give their children a good sex education. Others,
usually because of inadequacies of their own parents in this regard,
are not qualified for the job. Parental inadequacies of this nature
are often passed from one generation to the next.

Children are curious and do ask about sex. They should be
given truthful answers in language they can understand. At age
three, when the child asks where babies come from it is enough
to answer: "They grow inside mother's body in a special place

built for them." Straightforward answers without detailed information will satisfy him at this age. If his questions are answered adequately, he will return to the same source as he grows older and desires more exact information.

The sex questions of children will at times tax the ingenuity of parents, or perhaps shock them. Sex for a child is not charged with emotion. A parent who feels shame about sex will give information in such a way that the child will sense an embarrassment which he does not understand. Sex can in fact be so charged emotionally by parents that education will do little good. The authors have known a number of college students who, though willing to concede the facts of human reproduction at a theoretical level, refused to admit they were conceived and delivered in that fashion.

When human biology is taught, the reproductive system should be discussed along with other systems. Just before age eleven, however, some special sex teaching might advantageously take place. This is the age at which the highest intellectual capacity exists before the emotions, embarrassment, and anxiety created by personal sexual maturation and drives impede learning. Furthermore, adolescents may be either troubled or falsely assured by misconceptions relating to sex. Some formal instruction should be provided from reputable professional sources. Because human sexual behavior is variable and affected by learning and social conditioning, there is some concern that sex education will increase participation in sexual activities. There is no evidence to support this view. But there is evidence that students who have the widest and most accurate sex knowledge find it easier to date and to acquire superior social skills. Those with limited knowledge feel inadequate, awkward, and tend immediately to become too serious with the first boy or girl they meet.

Adolescents are also looking for standards of sexual behavior. Parents owe it to their children to delineate (and give by example) those which they practice and believe, and would like their children to practice and believe, with as many facts and arguments as they can muster to support their case. Religions, too, should invite discussions of the standards they recommend and of the philosophy behind them. Standards which are simply imposed usu-

ally receive either blind support or lip service—in either case an
insecure base for understanding an action.

sex and society

What does the adolescent learn from society? One thing is
immediately apparent. Advertising is loaded with vicarious sex
symbols and sexual postures. Paperbacks, motion pictures, and television all trade on sex. This vicarious exploitation of the inhibited
sexual drive is designed not only to stimulate sexual needs, but
to convert and channel them toward purchase of the "symbols" of
sex.

Even casual observation reveals some confusion. There is a
difference between the way people advise and expect an adolescent
to behave, and the way they behave themselves. There is also a
difference between what constitutes acceptable sexual behavior
for men and for women. A boy may be warned against prostitutes,
but tacitly advised by his father and more actively by his peers as
to how he might safely sow his "wild oats." In addition, he learns
there is almost universal involvement in sexual expression and
much variety of conduct. What is acceptable conduct for one social
group may not be for another. In one group, his ideas about
sex are too advanced, but in order to be accepted by another
group he would have to have experienced intercourse. At present,
about all he gets from society is a feeling of confusion and many
unanswered questions.

It is clear that each adolescent's needs and expectations from
sex and love are peculiar to him. They derive from his experiences
during the various phases of psychosexual development, from his
sex education and from the attitudes about sex which prevail in
his home, church, and social segment of society. There are as
many different kinds and degrees of needs in sex and love as there
are different kinds of people. That is why a single standard of
behavior cannot be applied to all. Yet every adolescent should
have some standard by which he accepts some modes of conduct
and rejects others.

sources of sexual outlet

Masturbation

Masturbation is conscious self-stimulation to effect erotic arousal, usually by manipulating the genitals. By this definition, more than 90 per cent of the males in the United States over fifteen years of age have engaged in some form of masturbation that leads to orgasm. Some males masturbate once or twice in their lives; others as much as twenty times per week for a long period of time. The average frequency in early adolescence is between two and three times per week. About 50 to 60 per cent of all females masturbate to orgasm, but usually no more than once or twice a month. For the young, masturbation is the chief source of sexual outlet up to marriage.

The great majority of physiologists and clinicians agree that masturbation does no physical harm. Some authorities caution against carrying it to excess. They make plain, however, that they do not mean physical excess. Like many other physiological functions, erotic response depends on a fool-proof mechanism—one reaches a limit of physiological endurance and no longer responds erotically. And so with masturbation. The male, for example, must experience an erection for satisfactory masturbation. If he does not respond erotically, there is no erection, no masturbation, and no excess.

The excess the scientists speak of is psychological. In this sense masturbation is excessive when it is substituted for other outlets to relieve tensions and anxieties which are not in the main sexually derived—like concern over one's schoolwork or job, rejection by peers or colleagues, uncertainties about self-worth, or the hostility generated by unsatisfactory husband-wife, courtship, or other interpersonal relationship. Only after masturbation is begun to reduce these tensions, is sexual phantasy introduced in an effort to place the act in a sexual framework; when an individual is masturbating in response to a sexual need, phantasy is what excites him to the act, not vice-versa. Another symptom of psychological excess is worry caused by masturbating more than one might wish. Adolescents do not especially like to masturbate, and they attempt to limit its practice. They may ration themselves to one or two experiences a week. And then in response to a series of sexually stimulating experiences they exceed their self-imposed rations, develop guilt feelings and begin to worry that they are losing control of a bad habit.

Part of the worry is caused by misconceptions. There are, alas, still those who believe masturbation "drives one crazy." What may be the origin of this belief is interesting. Uninhibited inmates of mental institutions often masturbate openly—this is a perfect example of the fallacy of *post hoc ergo propter hoc*—after this, therefore because of it. More common, however, is the false association of masturbation with acne, loss of weight, baldness, fatigue, impotence, or weak eyes. Youngsters, males in particular, experiment to determine the effect of frequency of masturbation on pimples. *No* relationship between any physical disorder and masturbation has ever been established.

Parents sometimes contribute to faulty thinking about the act. They believe it will do their child some harm, and they discourage him with threats of physical punishment and other dire consequences. In a few cases, the objection seems to originate in an unconscious resentment of the sexual maturity which masturbation reveals; it is a symbol of their children's growing up and of competing with them—son against father especially.

Those who masturbate say they feel let-down or depressed after the act. This is true after any kind of climax. The phantasy accompanying masturbation is exciting, and when the act is over, there is acute realization that it *was* phantasy and nothing more. Furthermore, the male ego is not strengthened by masturbation. It is strictly a consolation prize. He would rather be engaging in the intercourse visualized in the phantasy. There is let-down after an exciting basketball game or drama. All of these experiences have anticlimaxes. The excitement of masturbation also increases the blood pressure and heart rate; it is both exhilarating and exhausting. It is natural, therefore, for one to be emotionally and physically spent.

Another worry of those who masturbate is that they are being betrayed by physical symptoms; moist palms, acne, baldness, shadowy eyes. Common sense dictates that no one can tell by looking whether a person has been masturbating recently, or excessively, or at all. The male joking associated with the act serves perhaps to take the sting out of guilt feelings. However, in view of the high incidence and frequency of masturbation it is likely that one of these jokes will be leveled at a young man when it is directly applicable. That is, he *has* been masturbating and he therefore takes the taunts seriously.

Even when people know a great deal about masturbation, they may still be troubled by it as a habit. Most problems which develop from masturbation are not due to failures in knowledge but to deep conviction, sometimes religious, that masturbation is wrong or harmful. But the conviction does not prevent the act; it simply makes one worry about it all the more. And sometimes even though people have assured themselves intellectually of the acceptability of masturbation as an outlet, they unconsciously worry about it.

However, most persons negotiate masturbation in good mental and physical health. Consciously or not, they recognize that they are looking for more mature sexual activity. One indication that masturbation is transient lies in the phantasy usually associated with it. Most who masturbate phantasize about sexual relations or sex play with a member of the opposite sex or a symbolic embodiment whom they find exciting, and even though masturbating they are wishing for and anticipating some more satisfactory type of outlet. So long as masturbation is accompanied by phantasies of heterosexual relations, it may be contributing to psychosexual development; masturbation without phantasy is a sign that a person needs professional help to overcome a childish holdover impeding his psychosexual growth.

The male usually masturbates by manipulating his penis with his hands (sometimes simulating the phantasized vaginal pressure on the penis) or by creating friction between the penis and some other object. There are countless variations. Females (particularly the unmarried) masturbate by finger or thigh manipulation of the clitoris. They do not insert objects into the vagina as frequently as some popular sources would have one believe. Married females, or those who have had extensive intercourse are more inclined to masturbate vaginally, but even for them clitoral stimulation is the more usual method.

Most of those seeking counsel because they find masturbation a problem want to know how to cut down on frequency. For most persons there is a sequence of events, or stimulating conditions which lead to masturbation. These can run from pornographic articles and pictures, to urinary pressures, to constricting clothing like tight shorts, to dancing or necking. About the best advice that can be given is to avoid, minimize, or substitute something for the conditions which seem to lead to masturbation. For example, if being alone is one of these, more time should be sought for recreation. The sequence leading to masturbation should be analyzed and steps taken to interrupt it. Effort should also be made to understand why there is worry about masturbation. Perhaps periods of anxiety provoke excessive masturbation, or masturbation may be compensating for deprived or neglected needs in one's life. Sometimes recognition of this is enough to reduce or overcome the problem. If one cannot resolve it to his satisfaction, perhaps he should visit a counselor.

In any case, one should recognize masturbation for what it is—another hurdle in the psychosexual growing-up process; a temporary substitute for something ultimately more satisfying. It is normal and intermediate within the present framework of our society.

Some persons worry that it will be difficult to stop masturbating after marrying (and indeed this is an occasional problem). They feel that if it is satisfying now they will be reluctant to give it up then. But there is no comparison between climax in masturbation and climax in intercourse after successful sexual adjustment has been achieved, for the latter is infinitely more satisfying. Another concern of some males is that masturbation may reduce potency. There is no evidence to justify this worry. In fact, masturbation is rarely harmful to marriage. More often it constructively fills gaps when marital intercourse is not possible—because of pregnancy, travel, illness—or to equalize a difference in sexual appetite between husband and wife.

Nocturnal Emission

Nocturnal emissions are the result of dreams induced by sexual tensions. One dreams that he is engaging in a sexual experience and at some time during it has an orgasm. In the male there is an ejaculation and thus the common name "wet dream." The female experiences no ejaculation; but she does have the sexual dream with thigh play and often an orgasm (but not so often as the male).

Sexual dreams are common; almost everybody has them. In the female, however, they frequently stop short of intercourse. A girl may also repress the memory of a dream and deny that it occurred. Frequency varies with the individual and seems to be related to the amount of sexual tension, need, provocation, or stimulation one is experiencing. Sometimes the dreams are abetted by conditions which irritate the sex organs such as a full bladder, constricting clothing, irritated foreskin, vaginal discharge.

It is best that the nature of these dreams be clearly understood, especially by those youngsters who are reaching the age at which the dreams are likely to begin. It is difficult enough sometimes to distinguish between the real world and the dream world, especially with sex-related subjects. Although a male makes careful distinctions between love for a fiancée or girl friend and love for his mother or sister, the dream world can make these distinctions hazy. Consequently, he may find himself in a dream-world sexual experience with someone with whom he would not consciously wish to share the experience. This is disturbing enough in itself, but the fact that his dream is accompanied by physical evidence of reality, that is, ejaculation, makes the situation worse. Understanding sexual dreams reduces the fears and guilt feelings which usually follow them.

It is common for young people to experience dreams before understanding fully the adult techniques for sexual intercourse; nevertheless, orgasm occurs at that stage of the dream at which they believe climax should occur in their concept of intercourse. This may involve fondling the genitals or kissing, rather than penetration of the penis into the vagina.

There seems to be no basis for the statement that, lacking another outlet, nocturnal emissions will care for male sex needs. Nocturnal emissions do not preclude other outlets, or vice-versa. One may have intercourse just before retiring and then have an emission. Masturbating immediately before going to sleep may be followed by a similar experience.

It appears that these dreams are like the simple wish fulfillment dreams of childhood—those which represent the greatest needs of the moment. An interesting study was made of the dreams of conscientious objectors who were put on a minimum nutritional subsistence diet for experimental purposes during World War II. At first their dreams included sexual subjects, but as they grew hungrier, they dreamed more and more of food, until sex practically disappeared.

Little of a moral nature can be said about nocturnal emissions. They simply happen. Some do suggest cleansing one's mind of impure thoughts and thinking pure thoughts most of the day, especially immediately before retiring, so that dreams of a sexual nature are less likely.

Petting

Most young men and women pet. Petting ranges from handholding and kissing to deliberate stimulation of male and female erogenous zones, usually the breasts and genitals. In fact, some couples stimulate each other's genitals to orgasm, for in our society heavy petting is sometimes a substitute for intercourse.

One reason for petting is curiosity about the organs of the opposite sex, a curiosity held from early childhood that remains inhibited and unsatisfied. Another is the pleasure from stimulation of erogenous zones; another is the attempt to incorporate a physical exchange with affection, and the assurance that one is attractive to the opposite sex. The foreplay leading to sexual intercourse is also petting, and because of its close association with that act, petting is of serious concern, particularly for a girl and her parents. Their own experiences and those of their friends as young people are vivid reminders to feed their concern.

Sometimes petting is related to social acceptance. Certain groups have implied petting standards, and willingness to accept them, to a large extent determines one's place. There can be a rather calculating attitude about petting in that a girl may try to let a boy go far enough to hold his interest, but no further. For boy and girl alike, the more persons dated, the less necking and petting engaged in, at least in terms of extent. A certain amount of sequential scheduling goes on—that is, what a boy is allowed to do is determined by the number of times he has been out with a particular girl. She must diligently work at defining her place between being too easy or too hard to get.

In petting, the girl may set the limit and the boy is aggressive against it. Both may think this is as it should be. The boy often believes it is entirely up to the girl to decide how far the affair should go, and unfortunately so does the girl. Neither one seems to recognize a mutual responsibility.

Petting emphasizes the physical aspects of a relationship. There are couples, who, no matter what the occasion, will spend as much time as they can petting. To them it is the ultimate for any event. These are girls who are known to be easy and boys who for needs of their own are attracted to them. To some extent this is a reflection of their need or hunger for affection; it may also, however, reveal their inability or unwillingness to explore and develop other areas of their personalities. Willingness to pet, is, of course, one way for a girl to gain certain popularity and assurance that she is a desirable love object. For the boy the "easy conquest" may spare him the competition for other and perhaps more suitable girls, and the risk of coming in second best, or, even after extending himself, of failing altogether.

No one knows when petting will lead to intercourse. The trembling moment of decision is always in delicate balance. Sexual excitement is progressive and difficult to stop short. One test of how far to go in petting is defining the point at which one begins to lose respect for oneself or for one's partner. It is usually the boy who thinks less of the girl (some types of petting and the girl's response may conflict with his image of motherhood). Whenever ones does anything which degrades another human being, he has gone too far. One should think clearly—*beforehand*—of what this "cut-off" point is and stop short of it. Preferably this should be a decision involving both partners, so they both know when to slow down and stop.

Intercourse

Misconceptions about premarital relations should be quickly dispelled. Some claim that premarital sex experience is essential to health. There is no evidence that lack of this experience entails a handicap to physical or emotional development. There is also speculation that premarital intercourse reduces the supply of sperm cells which can be used legitimately in marriage, and that premarital promiscuity leads to postmarital promiscuity. Evidence controverts the first point and is missing for the second.

Whether or not to have premarital intercourse is a disturbing problem, perhaps more for the young woman than for the young man. Many young people do have intercourse before marriage and negotiate it satisfactorily. Others suffer conflicts which damage their personalities and marriage relationships. The determining effect seems to depend on how realistic they were in appraising their feelings and motivations about intercourse when they decided to experience it.

A large number of people feel that premarital sex relations are all right for the male but not for the female. The male may very much wish a virgin wife. He may attach special significance to being her first and only lover. He knows that with few exceptions a woman gives herself sexually only after an emotional commitment, and he does not wish to share this with anyone. He does not want to compete with the memory of her first lover. He may also feel that, if his wife has had intercourse with others, she may be comparing his performance with theirs. Women know that men value virginity, and may therefore wish to be virgins at marriage. Some women pretend that they are, and others wish so hard to be virgins that they even convince themselves.

The male ego is definitely involved here. In almost all societies, greater sexual freedom is a male prerogative. Often enough the most promiscuous, nondiscriminating male expects a virgin for a bride, and goes to unusual lengths to make sure he gets one. He may be one of those emotionally insecure men with little faith or trust in women, one who attributes his own weaknesses of character to the opposite sex. A woman may accept the fact that her husband is having relations outside marriage but does not think that she should. Even if she tries an affair she may learn through bitter experience that it does not work. Pride and self-esteem are tied so very closely to her sexual relations that they must have adequate emotional roots and some purpose to succeed. If these elements are missing, and she is simply trying to follow the sexual standards of men, she may be badly disappointed.

It is sometimes said that sexual outlet before marriage is needed more by the male than by the female, and that he can participate with less sentimental and emotional involvement than she. Some women do, in fact, want husbands with sexual competence and are not necessarily jealous of the other women their husbands have enjoyed. They sense that a man with experience has overcome his fear of women, and can accept with appreciation what a woman has to offer. They apparently feel safer with a man who has tested himself and knows how to please a woman.

But however valid the reasons for supporting a dual standard, there is a logical inconsistency about it. Premarital or extramarital intercourse is pretty much a one-to-one relationship—man and woman. Female prostitutes are no influence; in spite of heavy publicity, they are involved in only a small percentage of present-day extramarital experiences. And for each promiscuous woman, one can find a promiscuous male. The dual standard is philosophically interesting but unrealistic. When one believes that premarital or extramarital experience is permissible for the male, he must recognize it as potentially permissible for the female as well.

Couples who engage in premarital intercourse sometimes have what they hope is a meaningful talk about it beforehand. They talk about the need for sexual satisfaction, their relationship with one another, the possible undesirable consequences of intercourse, and the steps that can be taken to prevent some of these. They try to examine their feelings and motivations and what it will do to their relationship, then they may decide to go ahead. They may discover, however, that accepting a situation intellectually is not the same as accepting it emotionally, and that it did matter to their relationship. They may feel less respect for each other, particularly the boy for the girl. Deep down, perhaps unconsciously, he might find her less desirable, less to be sought after—like the loser in a competitive event.

On the other hand, some young people report that premarital sexual relations seem to draw them closer together, especially if they plan to be married. Incidentally, the only genuine *premarital* intercourse—we use the term loosely—is enacted by those unmarried persons who truly anticipate marrying each other. Most premarital intercourse is pre-nothing or is simply another way of saying *nonmarital* intercourse. Yet something which seems acceptable before marriage may be quite the opposite in retrospect. All too often a husband under the stress of marriage reproaches his wife for having relations before marriage even though he was her persuading partner.

The desirability of premarital revelations or "confessionals" should be weighed with an eye toward the motivation of the confessor and the impact this might have on the partner. Revelations are sometimes difficult to accept or understand out of the context of circumstances in which the experience took place. Those who before marriage tell about their previous sex experience may find these tales objectionable after marriage. In the heat of a quarrel or the smoldering resentment of a previously accepted but newly appraised premarital record, a lot of unpleasantness can occur.

According to one way of thinking a young man should be as aggressive as he can in persuading a young woman to have sexual relations. It is up to her to set the limits, for she is primarily responsible for whatever occurs. As we have said, both young men *and* young women feel this way. A real factor here is the apparent instinct in a girl's thinking of sex, pregnancy, and motherhood. Even in the early years of her psychosexual development, as soon as she accepts the role of a woman, she wishes to be a mother and have a child. Certainly she is at a greater social, emotional, and physical disadvantage if a premarital relationship sours.

The aggressive tactics of some males are often well-planned, even meticulously, if the girl's defenses are good. They might learn poetry, study special subjects of interest to the girl, and find a sudden passion for particular types of music, all to assist with the chase. Gifts, food, wines and liquor, shows, dances, college weekends are standard tools of conquest. Some feel that any girl can be "had." It is simply a matter of learning the right approach and persisting. It should be said, however, that behind the scenes some girls are subtly and flirtatiously leading the young man on in order to obtain these favors.

Others have found that it saves time to tell the girl they love her. And, they reason, why shouldn't they tell them, if it will hasten the end? Of course, the girl might ask if he *really* loves her. She may be only pretending to herself that the boy is sincere. But with the avowal of love a relationship seems to become something special, above reproach. Women can be so successful in explaining love to themselves that they are self-deluded. Or here again they can lead a young man on by professing what they do not genuinely feel in order to gain him as a lover.

Another difficulty with "love" as an influence in deciding about intercourse is the rapidity with which young people fall in and out of love (in and out of engagements and pinning). This type of "love" is known for shifting to boredom or dislike. Much reproach-ment and downgrading of self and others after a broken love affair originates in the sharing of sexual intimacies.

Young men and women with training, knowledge, and insight on their side should join in evaluating a relationship and in taking responsibility for setting the limits and the consequences of their own actions. A decision as important as premarital relations should certainly have the sincere and honest consideration of *both* partners. Otherwise deceit, shame, emotional confusion, and disillusionment take over—sometimes before, sometimes after.

There are other obvious hazards in premarital relations, among them conception, loss of social reputation, and venereal disease.

Conception

In spite of the deterrent power of the fear of an out-of-wedlock pregnancy, an increase in the number and ratio of unwed mothers among teenagers is expected during the 1960's. In the United States from 1938 to 1958 the estimated annual number of illegiti-mate births rose from 88,000 to 209,000, with the largest increase among women aged twenty-five to twenty-nine. Contrary to popular belief, unwed mothers come from widely separate socio-economic levels. The problem is not limited to a few groups of particular educational, racial or religious backgrounds; it is found everywhere in our society.

No matter what caution is exercised, pregnancy is always pos-sible. No contraceptive is foolproof. Even the condom, the most practical for premarital intercourse, has been known to fail if badly made or misused. The douche attempts to wash sperm cells out of the vagina, but is even less trustworthy. Fear of pregnancy inhibits the enjoyment of sex relations, even for some married women who do not wish an unplanned pregnancy. It is worse for the unmarried woman, for as a result of worry she may find present sexual relations too disturbing and unsatisfactory to overcome this memory easily and enjoy them later on in marriage.

If conception does take place, she must then either undergo an induced abortion or bear the child. Concern over conception is debilitating in itself. The menstrual cycle can be disrupted by anxiety; the girl who worries about pregnancy may actually produce a temporary delay in her menstrual period, even though she is not pregnant.

Abortion is illegal and, as we have learned, if the girl places herself in the hands of unqualified people, her ability to have children later on may be impaired. Or the whole experience might be so distasteful as to leave serious psychological scars.

If the girl bears the child, she may have to marry the father. It is estimated that the bride is "expecting" is about one in four marriages. If he is reluctant, the marriage may be forced. Those marriages seldom work well. She can go to a home for unwed mothers or be sent to a distant city until her child is born. Neither solution is satisfactory. One does not have to accentuate here the difficult role for the illegitimate child or the stigma of being an unwed mother. Once again the woman bears the burden. Although biologically he is half the cause of the illegitimacy, the man may remain aloof. His pursuit of sexual favors during courtship is acceptable evidence of his masculinity, but the female's granting of such favors is evidence of her lack of skill in retaining her suitor without losing her virginity. There is no phrase equivalent to "fallen woman" applicable to the male. He seldom pays for the abortion, if there is one, or for the custodial care if she has the child. He makes no effort to get the girl married, if he does not marry her himself. Furthermore, his parents largely ignore any responsibility for the affair. Without question, one obligation of partners in premarital experience is to guard against conception. Whoever fails to do this either does not care about the other person or is too immature to appreciate the grave social consequences—in either case an undesirable partner.

Social Reputation

Unfortunately a large number of youngsters exaggerate and broadcast the details of their sexual experience. They do not appreciate how damaging to reputations such indiscriminate talking might prove. A girl who yields in the intimacy of what she considers to be a very personal relationship is distressed to learn that her partner has told his best friends and maybe anyone else who would listen. Some male egos are nurtured in this way; and they do not wish their conquests to go unheralded. Whoever cannot keep his own counsel in an affair is too immature to engage in one.

Venereal Disease

The name *venereal disease* is related to the *mons veneris,* an area of the female pelvis under the pubic hair. This area is obviously associated with sexual intercourse, the primary method for transmitting the disease. The male and female genital organs are the most common sites of infection and sexual intercourse the primary means of transmittal. Of all the venereal diseases, syphilis and gonorrhea are the most prevalent. At the present writing they represent the largest and most serious communicable disease problem in the United States. It is estimated that fully 10 per cent of the adult population has been infected with one or both of these diseases, sometimes with disastrous results.

Syphilis: Syphilis has a long history. Evidences of it have been found in skeletons uncovered in archaeological expeditions. Some claim it was introduced to Europe by Columbus' crew soon after their return from the discovery of America. In the next several centuries, it rampaged through Europe and eventually became a major affliction throughout the world, a status that it still holds.

The origin of syphilis has always been in lively dispute. Each country gave credit to another, and syphilis was called French pox, Italian pox, English pox, and so forth, depending on the source of the literature. It was consistently called the pox because of the symptoms (pustules that resemble large pimples or blisters) that break out in an early stage of the disease. Reliable information about the cause of syphilis, however, does not exist before 1903 when, following the development of the microscope and the science of bacteriology, the corkscrew-shaped microorganism (*treponema pallidum*—a member of the spirochete family) causing the disease was isolated.

The spirochete is very fragile and dies quickly outside the body. It is readily killed by drying and is unusually susceptible to heat, but has been known to live up to two hours on wet surfaces.

Although syphilis *can* in theory be transmitted by use of a common drinking glass, toilet seat, etc., it is highly unlikely. The disease is most often spread by direct contact, usually during sexual intercourse or in foreplay of the type which precedes intercourse.

Spirochetes which cause infection are present in the fluid of an ulcer-like sore (chancre) or other open sores of the diseased person. Chancres are usually located on the genital organs, lips or tongue, but they and other open sores can be situated on almost any part of the body. The spirochete penetrates the skin or mucus membranes at the point of contact through minute abrasions and probably even through the intact surface. Minute abrasions during sexual intercourse can be caused by the friction of contact of the genital organs and cuts or scratches caused by the pubic hair. The spirochete does, however, require appreciable time to penetrate the membrane or skin, and the application of prophylactic treatment soon after exposure may prevent infection. If infection sets in and is allowed to go untreated syphilis will follow in four stages: primary, secondary, latent, tertiary.

The first symptom of primary syphilis is the appearance of a chancre at the place where the spirochete entered the body, in most instances on or around the genitals. In women it is frequently found inside the vagina in an area not easily seen (even in a vaginal examination by a physician), and causes little discharge or discomfort. In men it may appear in the folds of the foreskin or at the underside of the penis. Even if observed, the chancre, though sizeable, can be trifling in appearance, painless, and subject to little attention. It is entirely possible to have an open chancre and infect other people without knowing it.

The chancre usually appears from ten days to three weeks, but sometimes as long as ninety days, after infection. It lasts one to three weeks and heals with or without treatment—in the latter case leaving a small scar. While the chancre is present syphilis is largely confined to the area around it.

The secondary stage of syphilis, about three to eight weeks after the appearance of the chancre, is revealed in a generalized skin eruption resembling measles or chicken pox. It may cover the entire body including the palms of the hands, soles of the feet, and the mucus membranes of the mouth, nose, throat and vagina. The rash is painless and may be so mild as to be mistaken for heat or drug rash, and thus escape serious concern. It can clear up without treatment and many persons even at this stage have syphilis without knowing it. The spontaneous termination of the chancre and the rash can be unfortunate. The infected person might believe himself cured and fail to seek treatment.

During the secondary stage the disease spreads generally through the body. The bloodstream may carry the spirochete anywhere—joints, eyes, internal organs, spinal cord, and brain. The infected person may feel slightly ill with sore throat, fever, and headaches. Hair sometimes may fall out in patches. These symptoms clear up within four to six weeks. In the meanwhile the spirochete is imbedding itself in the deeper tissues, and the disease is progressing to the latent stage.

At the end of the secondary stage there is a complete freedom of symptoms, which might last from a few months to twenty years. This freedom is known as the latent stage of syphilis. However, the disease is far from latent, and the spirochetes are effecting great destruction.

As soon as some symptoms of this destruction manifest themselves, the disease is in the tertiary and final stage. The symptoms of this stage are so varied and diversified that few are illustrative. Generally speaking they involve the bony structures, circulatory and nervous systems, and can result in blindness, insanity, crippling, heart trouble, paralysis, and finally death. Statistics show that among untreated syphilitics, 1 in 200 go blind, 1 in 50 become insane, 1 in 25 become crippled and 1 in 15 develop blood vessel and heart trouble symptoms.

In a small fraction of cases the body's own defenses against the disease are successful. Some persons, inadequately treated or not at all, will never have the disease develop to the tertiary stage. For those in whom the disease has reached this stage, little can be done to repair the destruction, but usually further damage can be arrested.

The most tragic victim is the unborn child who contracts syphilis from his mother. Although syphilis cannot be inherited, the spirochete can pass the placental barrier and infect the child in the uterus (congenital syphilis). If the mother receives treatment before the fifth month of pregnancy, the child will probably not be harmed. The longer treatment is delayed beyond the fifth month, the poorer his chances. Tissue may be destroyed, resulting in bodily defects, a heart condition, skin eruptions, brain damage, or he may die in the uterus. Of course, any treatment in any stage of pregnancy is better than none.

In an effort to prevent congenital syphilis, the law now requires a physician to take blood tests on pregnant women in his care. (And here is another good reason for reporting to a physician early in pregnancy.) Happily, as a result of such laws and intensive educational drives, congenital syphilis is decreasing.

There are various tests for syphilis. The secretions of chancres and other skin eruptions can be examined under the microscope for the presence of the spirochete. Blood tests, such as the Wassermann, may or may not be positive in the primary and tertiary stages, but are usually positive in the secondary and latent stages. The body in trying to fight the progress of the disease forms antibodies whose presence in the blood is the basis for most of these tests.

Syphilis, once diagnosed, must be treated actively and continuously until the person is no longer infected. A small revolution has occurred in treatment within the last twenty years. A long, somewhat dangerous, painful use of arsenical compounds has been replaced by a shorter, simpler, and more effective treatment with penicillin compounds—ten days to two weeks of massive doses will destroy the spirochete in most cases. And in the few cases where penicillin is ineffective other simple antibiotic treatments are available. Those treated should have periodic follow-up tests for at least two years.

It should be emphasized that treatment can almost always halt the further development of syphilis but it cannot repair those portions of organs which have already been destroyed. The earlier the treatment the better, and, of course, prevention is more desirable than any cure. No specific immunity exists; having syphilis once is no assurance that it will not be contracted again. However, the disease does seem to have become less severe for man over the centuries.

Gonorrhea: Gonorrhea is the most common of the venereal diseases. Like syphilis it has been a plague to the human race throughout its history. At least half a million fresh infections crop up in the United States each year, and there appears to be no downward trend.

Gonorrhea is caused by the gonococcus bacterium. Infection usually occurs during sexual intercourse, when the gonococci present in the genital organs of one partner make contact with the genital organs of the other. Indirect transmission of the disease is possible but improbable, for gonococci are extremely fragile and live only for a short period outside the body.

In men the disease attacks the mucus membrane lining the urethra and produces redness, swelling, and irritation. The first symptom of the disease is often a burning sensation with pain during urination, which begins two to six days after infection. This is followed by an infectuous, yellowish discharge from the penis. The pain is distressing enough to induce the patient to seek medical treatment.

A woman seldom notices any pain or other symptoms in the early stages of the disease. There is a discharge of pus from the vagina, but she might attribute this to nervousness, fatigue, ovulation with its increased mucus flow, or to a mild vaginal irritation having no serious meaning. Frequently, however, the infection spreads from the vagina to the urethra, and she then experiences the same painful symptoms at urination as the male.

If infection is mild, the incubation period before the symptoms appear might be prolonged beyond the usual two to six days. In that case, the symptoms may appear when the resistance is lowered by such conditions as fatigue or excessive drinking of alcohol.

Sometimes, *not always*, the disease, even if untreated, is combatted successfully by the body and clears up in a matter of a few weeks. This happens in the male more than in the female, for the numerous folds of the vaginal mucus membrane provide better protection for the gonococci. In some untreated cases the urethral symptoms disappear but the infection spreads internally—in the male along the linings of the reproductive and accessory organs: prostate, seminal vesicles, epididymides, and testes, producing a swollen painful condition—and in the female, to the cervix, Fallopian tubes, ovaries, and peritoneum of the pelvis. Unchecked, gonorrhea can cause sterility by blocking the reproductive passageways or by otherwise damaging essential organs, particularly in the female where adhesions involving the tubes and ovaries impair their functions. Occasionally, in both male and female, the disease breaks through local barriers and invades the bloodstream, carrying infection to various parts of the body and causing heart trouble, arthritis, blindness, or even death. Fortunately, despite the high incidence of the disease, this type of breakthrough is rare.

Once a person is infected, gonococci may persist in the genito-urinary system for years after apparent recovery, and the individual becomes a carrier. Although no longer noticeably present in the urethra the disease might be harbored in the prostate of the male and found in the semen at ejaculation, and gonococci may lurk in the crevices of the vagina, cervix, and urethra of the female.

There are two notable exceptions to infection by direct sexual contact. Young girls can contract gonorrheal vulvo-vaginitis through indirect contact—bedclothes, common bath tubs, and the like. Perhaps the greatest biological value of the hymen is protecting young girls against such vaginal infections until physiological maturity provides them with greater natural resistance. At puberty the vaginal membrane becomes heavier, thicker, and much more resistant to infection.

The eyes of newborn children can also be infected with gonorrheal ophthalmia during passage through the birth canal of an infected mother. As recently as 1950 about 10 per cent of all blindness was traceable to this source. At one time it was the most common cause of blindness. The present practice of applying medications to the eyes of newborn children has virtually eliminated this cause of blindness in the United States.

There is no practical blood test for gonorrhea. Diagnosis is made through microscopic examination for the presence of gono-cocci in the penile or vaginal discharges. Yet this is no foolproof test; a person may be infective, but gonococci may not be present in the specimen of discharge examined. Repeated tests may be necessary. Those interested in escaping detection, for example, prostitutes and service men subject to punishment can bathe the infected parts before examination, or otherwise wash the gonococci from the infected zones, making diagnosis difficult.

Like syphilis, most early cases of gonorrhea can be cured with penicillin or other antibiotics. But, again, there is no immunity. No known vaccine will protect against infection by gonorrhea or syphilis. A person who has had one of these diseases does not become immune to the other; in fact, he can suffer both at the same time.

The incidence of other venereal diseases is minor in comparison. *Chancroid* resembles in many ways the chancre of syphilis. The specific cause of this disease is as yet unknown, but it remains local, responds readily to treatment, and does not have the serious after-effects of syphilis. The *venereal wart (chandylomata)* is a cluster of wart-like growths around the genitals or rectal area. It is probably caused by a virus, like most other warts, and can be treated easily and effectively. These diseases also are usually but not always spread by direct sexual contact.

One way in which venereal disease is spread is through prostitution. The professional prostitute operating in a segregated district or commercialized house of prostitution can have from thirty to forty customers in twelve hours, the regular working shift. Over weekends and pay periods she may have as many as sixty to seventy in one shift. The vagina of the prostitute cannot possibly be kept uncontaminated. It is estimated that an infected woman will give the disease to approximately 50 per cent of her male contacts—twenty to thirty a day. Streetwalkers and B-girls have an average of three to four sex exposures a day. It is perhaps fortunate that they lose time in meeting customers and drinking with them before taking them to a place where the sexual act is consummated.

It is estimated that any woman who has worked as a prostitute for more than a year has contracted both syphilis and gonorrhea. Of all prostitutes who are correctly examined, 25 to 50 per cent are found to have a venereal disease; and even those who do not have demonstrable symptoms may be carriers. In addition, an earlier patron can infect a later one with the prostitute serving as the carrier.

Shocking though these statistics may be, more venereal disease is transmitted by sexual intercourse in casual relationships ("pick-ups") than by prostitutes. Recent surveys confirm that many more promiscuous relations go on outside of houses of prostitution than within them, many times involving people trying to satisfy a need for affection and security through sexual experience. Many unwary young men are infected in this way. Flattered, excited, and over-come by obtaining a partner, they fail to take preventive measures, whereas the prostitute and her client in full knowledge of the possibility of infection usually take precautions against it.

Homosexuality is an unexpectedly large factor in the transmission of venereal disease. In one community, 70 per cent of a group of boys fifteen to nineteen years old being treated for syphilis admitted that their contacts were exclusively homosexual. A similar pattern among male adults was shown in another study. The syphilis rate among homosexuals is six times that of other men.

Every state has laws that require the reporting of all cases of venereal disease. Nevertheless, at the urging of patients who do not wish to be embarrassed, many physicians do not comply. A national survey revealed that physicians are reporting only a small fraction of the cases they diagnose and treat. At least 10 per cent of the population undergoes blood tests for syphilis every year in connection with premarital or prenatal examinations, or hospital and clinic admissions. About 70 per cent of the cases of syphilis uncovered by these tests are reported to health authorities. In spite of the missing reports from these sources, it is evident that venereal disease is found in all sections of the country, in all age groups, in all income classes, and in all races.

Unfortunately for the health of the nation, the cases which are not reported cannot be followed up. When cases are reported, health authorities can identify those who have had contact with the infected person. Studies show that the average syphilis patient has sex relations with two or more persons during the infectious period and that one of them, or perhaps both, will get the disease. Within a short period of months, a chain reaction can transmit the infection from one person to fifty others. Even children can be included in this chain. A child revealed in one survey was six. Many people are reluctant to divulge the names of persons to whom they may have transmitted venereal disease, even though health authorities treat such information as confidential and conduct follow-up investigations with the utmost discretion. But shyness and a false sense of protectiveness here are out of place. The disastrous possibilities of an ever-multiplying chain reaction are obvious. It seems absurd to talk about "protecting" another person's reputation when silence may so seriously endanger his or her health and the health of others, including innocent family victims.

This chain reaction type of infection has become especially common among teenagers—their infectious syphilis rate has more than doubled in the last five years. There is a mixture of innocence and bravado—the latter sometimes a mask for fear and ignorance—

in the young. Facts intended to influence their behavior must be presented clearly, yet it is evident that teenagers do not all have the facts about venereal disease. Because of periods of successful control with antibiotics in the last twenty years, there has been a let-down in dissemination of facts. But even a continual campaign on the consequences and horrors of untreated venereal disease will probably not dissuade young people from exposure—even though they might worry about it more. Society has no satisfactory solution to the sexual needs of the adolescent and the unmarried. The past and present history of venereal disease is only a glaring example of the great problem society is faced with in trying to cope with the sexual needs of its members—especially the young.

Studies also reveal considerable sexual promiscuity among adults, single and married. It is interesting to note that when significant reductions were made in the incidence and seriousness of venereal disease, they were attributable not so much to changes in sexual practices as to more adequate presentation of the facts of the disease and its transmittal, and improvements in preventive and therapeutic methods.

As indicated earlier, prevention is always more desirable than treatment, however good. Those most available for the sexual act also make venereal disease most available. In any event, some general protective procedures should be followed with each exposure.

Before engaging in casual sexual relations a man should obtain a condom and prophylactic kit from a drug store. He should wash genitals thoroughly with soap and water, avoid handling the genitals before the condom is in place on the erect penis, withdraw the penis immediately after ejaculation before the erection is lost, make sure he grips the ring at the top of the condom on withdrawal to prevent slipping off. Both partners should immediately urinate (to wash out any infectious germs from the urethra) and wash thoroughly the genitals and all exposed areas (chancres can be on areas not covered by the condom, e.g., testicles or inner thigh) with soap and water, as warm as is available and can be tolerated. These areas should be thoroughly dried. The male should then squeeze one half of the contents of the prophylactic tube into the urethra and smear the remaining half of the medication over the lining and skin of the organs which touched during intercourse. About all the female can do is make sure the male follows these instructions. Douching is not particularly helpful for her. Washing is somewhat more helpful, but there is no prophylactic kit for the female.

It is urgent that prophylaxis be applied as soon after intercourse as possible. The longer it is delayed, the less effective it will be. After two hours it may not be effective at all. Even so, better to use it then than not at all.

Precaution and prophylaxis interfere with pleasure in sexual intercourse and are messy. But they are not nearly so unpleasant as the consequences of venereal disease. A person mature enough to engage in sexual intercourse owes it to himself, his family, his partner, and society to be sensible enough to use prophylactic techniques to avoid getting or transmitting venereal disease.

Summary—Premarital Relations

If a partner to a sexual experience is too immature to guard against conception, loss of social reputation, and venereal disease, he or she is too immature to be participating in the experience.

Ultimately the decision whether or not to have premarital relations rests with the individual. The criteria come from various sources, personal and religious convictions and ethical values among them; or they might grow out of advance self-examination. Will one partner think less of the other afterward? Will it alter their impression of each other as potentially desirable marriage partners? If so, sexual relations are probably undesirable. Any relationship which disparages the human beings involved is faulty.

Generally speaking, premarital relations cannot be carried out with complete satisfaction in our society. Any basically mutual interest is enhanced as it is shared. The more it is shared, the more it joins the people sharing it. The same seems to be true of sex relations. Married women report that it takes three to five years of sexual intimacies with their husbands before they gain maximum satisfaction. Premarital experiences can seldom be shared to this extent. For this reason premarital relations are not a good barometer for estimating the sexual outlook in marriage.

An experience is more meaningful if it contributes to a total relationship. People who share each other's embrace for sexual pleasure alone probably never get the depth of satisfaction enjoyed by those who have additional reasons for the embrace—shared interests, ideals and goals, respect for each other. In other words, complete experience.

However, young people can feel very romantic about each other and want to believe that they have a total relationship. Sexual attraction can easily override deeper and more responsible considerations in evaluating a potential marriage partner. Youngsters can mistake sexual appetite for the whole of love rather than a part of it. For them, premarital sexual experience sometimes turns out to be not so total or so satisfying as they expected. When the sexual aspect is achieved, no other consideration remains in bold relief, and they realize that all they wanted was sexual accommodation. If a relationship is so limited as this, it should be discovered before marriage. But from a physical and emotional point of view, there must be better ways.

Intercourse with Prostitutes

One type of sexual experience without pretense of anything beyond sexual gratification is intercourse with a prostitute. Although the incidence of such intercourse is high, the frequency is low. Those who engage in it do so only once or a few times in their lives.

There are four kinds of prostitutes: male and female heterosexual, and male and female homosexual. But, by far the most common is the female prostitute who is paid by the male for her favors.

Prostitution does not have the social significance some would attribute to it. Most female prostitutes stay in the business only a short time; eventually they marry and fit into the social pattern. Prostitution is mostly a part-time practice, evening or weekend work to supplement income from full-time employment. For the most part prostitutes do not seek or derive sexual satisfaction from their clients; the act is performed mechanically, devoid of emotional meaning.

Legalized prostitution as a solution to many sex problems is sometimes suggested. Its advocates believe that if prostitutes are periodically examined for venereal disease and established in licensed brothels, then a legitimate and desirable sexual outlet will

130 PSYCHOSEXUAL DEVELOPMENT

be available for the male, thus assuring the sanctity of the majority of women who would otherwise be exploited. One difficulty with this theory is that there is no way to guarantee freedom from venereal disease. Another difficulty is that most people seek sexual outlet in the context of a more full relationship. They object to paying continually for sexual favor alone; they find it unsatisfactory. Men do not generally think of kissing prostitutes. However, it is kissing and love play that help make relations most satisfactory. The few men who visit prostitutes regularly either do not know how to establish a full relation with a woman, or do not wish to.

Surroundings at brothels can be unpleasant. A disgusted visitor may find himself fearful and impotent. The prostitute may become irritated and show it. He begins to worry that he will be impotent in other circumstances, and he could be, simply because worry over impotence is one of the best ways to produce it. Some men also have a combined fear and awe of women that may be reinforced by unsatisfactory experiences with prostitutes. Or they may develop antagonism and contempt for women, making satisfactory adjustment to a wife more difficult.

Homosexuality

Homosexuals are those whose orientation toward their reproductive functions and social sex roles has not been properly channeled. For this discussion a homosexual is defined as one who as an adult has physical contacts with another person of the same sex and who is brought to orgasm as a result of such contacts. Homosexuality is rigorously condemned by most people, social forces, and organizations, primarily because it is incompatible with the sexual drives and outlets of the majority, and with the family system and its aim of procreation.

Some who defend homosexuality or who ask for an objective view say it is wrong *only* because it is condemned by society. Such a condemnation, however, is a significant reason for judging it to be wrong. Defenders also point to societies in which homosexuality was or is accepted, but it seems unwise to isolate one practice in one society and attempt to transplant it to another, theoretically or practically. The results are open to too much interpretation. In fact, homosexual behavior is not the predominant type of sexual activity for adults in any society.

Earlier in this chapter we mentioned homosexual manifestations in the early adolescence phase of psychosexual development. The homosexual for various reasons does not develop beyond this stage, and behavior that may be appropriate or tolerable at one level, becomes a "perversion" at another. The evolution of homosexuality is probably most influenced by environment. Biological maturation accounts only for sexual drive; learning accounts for its direction. For example, while there is no evidence that homosexuality is caused by a glandular disorder, the development of overt homosexuality is found most often in men and women who consciously or unconsciously fail to sever family ties, who cannot establish a normal degree of independence from their parents.

The Freudian concept of the causes of homosexuality bears well on this point. In most cases the homosexual as a child had an overbearing, domineering, aggressive mother and a passive withdrawn father, who was not an adequate or desirable male to identify with at the end of the genital phase. As mentioned in the previous discussion of psychosexual development, one of the solutions of the genital phase, usually at the unconscious level, is the identification with the parent of the same sex. But the overbearing mother will make it difficult for the son to identify with his father and his masculine role. Instead the son identifies with the mother and becomes either a passive homosexual who puts himself into his mother's place and wants to be loved like his father loves his mother, or an active homosexual who gives another man the love and treatment he would like to have received from his mother. This latter behavior also holds for the female homosexual who gives her partner the love and treatment she would like to have received from her mother. Underneath this acting out of a love relationship resides a hatred and fear of the mother that keeps the homosexual dependent on his parents and on the people with whom he acts out this relationship.

There are two general types of homosexuals—transient and permanent. Although either may be equally obnoxious to some people, the transient homosexual is less of a social problem. *Transient* describes one who utilizes homosexual outlets in the absence of heterosexual outlets or who does so for a limited period in his life—for example, the prisoner who reverts to heterosexuality when released, or the soldier far from civilization. His action may be reprehensible and punishable if he is caught but he poses no baffling social question. Another type of transient homosexual may engage in heterosexual outlets as well. He may even be married, but occasionally seek relations with his own sex. He becomes a serious problem to society when his abnormal activity interferes with his marriage. It is interesting to note that some youngsters who find themselves seduced claim they did not suspect their seducer to be a homosexual because he "liked girls" or was married. Wives of these ambivalent men usually are aware of these tendencies in their husbands and live in fear of the detection and its consequences.

The permanent homosexual, on the other hand, prefers sexual experiences with his or her own sex, to the exclusion of the other. Young males with tendencies of this nature are upset by descriptions of heterosexual intercourse in much the same way that some heterosexual youngsters can be upset by descriptions of homosexual practices. The permanent homosexual creates a distinct social dilemma because he or she does not fit into the family pattern, and frequently gets involved in temporary relationships which dissolve in emotional and social chaos. Their pattern is different from that of heterosexual people. While two homosexuals may live with each other for years, they do not have sexual relations with each other exclusively over a long period. Love objects change continually, in many cases weekly or daily.

Homosexuals of either type, however, do not fit a general description; they have no particular set of characteristics. A homosexual male is sometimes effeminate, but all effeminate males are not homosexuals, and some masculine-looking and -acting men are. A few compulsive exhibitionists dress as members of the opposite sex and are quite open about their interests, but they are in the minority. Homosexuals are said to be found in disproportionately large numbers in certain professions. Little evidence supports this allegation. They do, however, tend to live in urban areas, where privacy and contacts are more easily found.

A common question is what to do when approached by a homosexual. One sound policy is to indicate firmly a lack of interest.

Some men feel threatened and want to display their masculinity by physically hurting the seducer. Extreme physical actions are unnecessary. If lack of interest is made clear, the pursuit will prove uncomfortable and end quite simply.

Homosexuality is not easily cured, if by this is meant changing the interest to heterosexuality. Once a pattern is established and the person defines himself as a homosexual, he seldom wants or seeks help. He enjoys his way of life and considers it natural, even though other people say it is not. Even those who want help may not seek it for fear of the consequences of revealing themselves as homosexuals. For homosexuals who seek psychotherapy, the possibility of being able to change is influenced by the strength of their motivation to change, and by their age and extent of homosexual experience. The earlier help is sought, the more successful it is. At the very least, a better social adjustment can be achieved so that a homosexual can work to earn a living, and not make sexual advances where they are unwelcome. If the motivation for treatment is strong, a skilled therapist can do much to restore the individual to a more fulfilling way of life.

The homosexual is generally despised, feared, and avoided, perhaps unreasonably so. Some claim that this extreme reaction occurs because latent homosexuality exists in so many persons who fear it might come to the fore. In any case, society tolerates homosexuality in women more so than in men who may discard their social responsibilities (taking care of and supporting women and children) as a result, or whose ethical or professional responsibilities make them more vulnerable to the attacks of people who know they have "something to hide."

alternate means of sexual expression

If the adolescent sex drive is not released through one of these outlets, then how? Three alternatives have been suggested: continence, sublimation, early marriage.

Continence

History and surveys of sexual behavior both confirm that prolonged continence is possible but too much to expect of most adults. Yet some people seem to practice it successfully. Of these, some are, hormonally or emotionally, sexually dormant—that is, have no strong sexual drive. On the other hand, the majority do have the urge but willfully *choose* not to seek an outlet, because of religious or ethical scruples, and seem quite happy about their decision. These people commonly experience nocturnal emissions.

No evident physical harm comes from continence. Some psychology teaches that repressed sex is dangerous. But *repressed* is a technical term: it does not mean suppressed in the sense of denied or resisted. Perhaps the sexually dormant person has repressed sex, for a repressed desire or thought is one which has been thrust into the subconscious and can now come before the mind only in a disguised and unrecognizable form. Repressed sexuality does not appear to be sexuality at all. When a person is actually engaged in resisting a conscious desire, he is not dealing with a repression, nor is he likely to be in danger of creating one.

Sublimation

Sublimation, sexually speaking, is the channeling of sexual energy into other outlets acceptable to the individual and society. It is claimed that if a person is active creatively, some of this energy derives from the sex drive. Although sublimation probably will never be a substitute for the whole of sexual impulse, considerable positive creative efforts and ambitions seem to owe much of their success to this source. If one keeps creatively occupied, the sex drive can be more manageable. This seems to be especially true today, when the opportunity for creativity is often absent. When family life, school, or vocation hold no promise of stimulation and achievement, no joy of craftsmanship, no sense of dignity from a job well done, then young persons are susceptible to sporadic diversions in sexual affairs, which temporarily relieve monotony.

Early Marriage

In our society actual marriage comes considerably later than biological readiness for it. It is therefore urged that narrowing this gap will solve much of the premarital sex problem.

The unfortunate paradox is that the condition of our society will probably lengthen the gap. Biological maturity cannot be postponed; but society becomes increasingly complex; more education and training are necessary to earn a living—so essential for marriage. Furthermore, our high standard of living, with decreased financial responsibility on the part of the young, may be prolonging immaturity in youngsters. They are given many of the things their forebears had to get for themselves. They are more closely regulated—passed from home to church to school to community, with less opportunity for independent action and growth.

Relying on early marriage as a solution to premarital sex problems is unrealistic. But one positive step is to help young people to maturity by letting them grow so that they can think for themselves and use information and experience wisely. Young adults are not looking for license so much as for guideposts. Foundations for guideposts are in some measure fixed by the time decisions about sexual matters are made.

Young adults who navigate well the difficult years of decisions about sexual conduct and outlets have some characteristics in common. They come from homes in which they felt secure and accepted, and in which they were taught to assume responsibility for their own actions. They were encouraged to exercise a healthy concern for their own emotional and physical needs and *for those of others.* This reduces the likelihood that they will have their own needs exploited, or that they will exploit the needs of others. They were helped to identify their goals, ambitions, and values in order to form perspective for deciding what is important now and in the future. But above all, their parents were examples of a man-woman relationship of warmth, affection, responsibility, and helpfulness. In contrast, the young people whose sexual conduct gets them into trouble have parents who because of their own emotional deprivations and inadequacies (and mostly in spite of good intentions) pass these qualities on to their children like an inherited disease.

preparation for marriage

CHAPTER FOUR

SEX AND LOVE are brought to fulfillment in the institution of marriage. Marriage channels sexual outlet toward creative and constructive goals for the partners and for society. It protects the pregnant female, and gives children the security they need until ready to go out on their own. It establishes the family, the basic unit of our way of life, and creates a sense of responsibility toward society's rules and regulations. It is for these reasons that society through its channels of control—the law, the church, the school, and the family unit itself—has surrounded marriage with an aura of strength and sanctity and the permanence of a nearly unbreakable contract. Through pressures from these institutions one is made to feel the desirability and seriousness of assuming the responsibilities of marriage. From childhood on we look forward with hope and anticipation to marriage as the most desirable state in which to live. In fact, marriage is the most sensible and satisfying economic, psychological, and physical arrangement for most people, and will remain so for the foreseeable future.

Most persons marry or expect to; 70 per cent of the American population fifteen years of age and over is married. But there are signs of instability and unhappiness: for every four marriages there is one divorce, and one poll reported that only 45 per cent of all married people would choose the same spouse if they had the chance again. Those who are alarmed at these signs blame the changing social scene. Others point to inadequacies in our courtship system, and admonish young people to choose their mates more wisely.

changing social scene

The emerging and expanding role of women, their increasing opportunities for work and financial independence, the greater personal fulfillment from marriage demanded by both spouses, population mobility and shifts to cities, diminished parental control and authority—all have combined with other social forces to upset the traditional ways of marriage. Critics of change feel we have severed our moorings to the old, but have not yet anchored to the new, and that marriage is "floating in midstream, buffeted by crosscurrents and confusions. . . ."

History reveals that the institution of marriage never has been static. We must expect changes and accompanying periods of instability. Our kind of marriage—one man to one woman (monogamy)—is relatively new and rare. In 85 per cent of the societies of the world today, men are permitted by custom to have more than one mate at a time. In a manner scarcely to be found in earlier history, sexual outlet, love, respect, companionship, childbearing and -rearing are all combined in a single relationship.

Even more novel is the acceptance of romantic love as the adequate and primary basis for choosing one's spouse. So firmly is this now established that it may be surprising to learn that it has not always been so. Romantic love as a basis for marriage did not come into western culture until the twelfth and thirteenth centuries. In the retrospect of time, romantic marriage is a relatively new social experiment, still confined to a minority of the world's people. Small wonder, then, that occasional signs of instability appear.

Even more importantly, however, the nature of marriage *should* change if it is to serve well the evolving needs of people and society. Such change should not be mistaken for instability. Were the traditions of marriage unyielding and the prescriptions rigid, they would bind and chafe more than they do, and more people would seek relief. On the positive side, changes (e.g., equal assignments of rights and responsibilities to both partners) have great potential for bringing marriage to higher levels of fulfillment.

In order to minimize the number of unhappy marriages and to bring about greater fulfillment, one must select a mate wisely. Courtship is our method of making this selection.

courtship system

Marital choice is perhaps the most important decision of a lifetime. Its effects are lasting and highly significant, not only for the well-being and happiness of the couple, but also for the welfare of their children, and for society as a whole.

In our society, both the privilege and responsibilities of marital selection are put directly in the hands of the potential partners, yet the choice faces them at a time when they are unlikely to be prepared to make such a weighty decision. They have had only limited experience to assist them and almost no previous opportunity to make major decisions. Few of them understand the full implications of marriage and the effort necessary to make it work. Generally they need help in thinking things through. But who can help?

Parental influence is not too significant after adolescence. In a material way, parents may prepare their sons and daughters for courtship and marriage: teeth straightening, decent wardrobes, pleasant neighborhoods, good educational and social opportunities are illustrative. But when the children are old enough to reach a decision about a mate, they must make it themselves (and live with it). The material in this chapter may suggest some guidelines.

The courtship process consists of progressive stages, each of which brings the individual closer to marriage. It begins with dating, usually extending through the teen years, during which time young people become acquainted; they develop general social skills, satisfy their needs for status with their peers, and give some thought to the idea of marriage and family. At some point dating intensifies, is limited to fewer members of the opposite sex, and ultimately to one. Engagement is the final step in courtship, wherein the future partners have the chance to become more thoroughly acquainted and determine their suitability for each other and their readiness for marriage.

Engagement is usually accompanied by a formal declaration

of intent to marry. The means for communicating this intent vary with group and setting. On the college campus the symbol of engagement might be either a fraternity pin or an engagement ring. Whether announced in the newspapers, at a party, or simply by word of mouth, it is an official testing of the pair under the scrutiny of the public eye.

In our society, engagement is as close as we come to a trial period of marriage. Success in engagement is the best single forecast of successful marriage. The length of engagement· does not matter so much as the efficiency with which the couple uses the period to find out more about each other. It is the time for placing one another under final scrutiny, to learn where the other partner stands on issues and activities vital to marriage. They should go swimming without bathing caps and look at each other as they come out of the water. They should discuss personal deficiencies from scars and birthmarks, to false teeth and "falsies." In the nature of things there is a certain amount of "cover up." This is an understandable human tendency which is tolerable if not excessive. But the fewer surprises after marriage, the better. One should make every effort neither to be a surprise package nor to acquire one.

Courtship is not always used wisely. All the niceties are observed, the bland things said, and, through skillful avoidance of any controversial subject, the impression created of nice, adjustable creatures with pleasing personalities who are sure to get along with each other. This requires a sort of social maneuvering, little of which touches on those things so essential to living together for decades in one of life's most intimate relationships—such things as, for example, what one thinks of religion, the working wife, family budget, childspacing, and the baby who needs exhausting round-the-clock care. Some young people seem to make a deliberate effort not to know each other better, afraid perhaps that they will find out something to endanger the romance.

Romantic love is generally blamed for such misuse. As stated earlier, one of the most distinctive current emphases regarding marriage is the high premium set upon romantic attraction—that one marries solely for love, that marriage is the realization of romance. In essence, most objections to romantic love as the basis for marriage stem from concern that young people are looking for the "one person in the world" with whom they will "fall in love at first sight," and that a "lightning courtship" dominated by "love is blind" will propel them into a hasty, ill-conceived marriage. How valid are these objections?

Without doubt, romantic love in courtship encourages some couples to misuse the courtship. They accentuate each other's desirable characteristics and overlook those annoying traits so apparent to friends and parents. Each partner feels troubled that his own weaknesses are not observed but does not try hard to expose them. Nevertheless romantic love as a disadvantage to courtship is probably not so widespread or serious as most critics think. In recent decades research findings have shown that however strong the faith of Americans in romantic love, it is far from being a faith pure and unalloyed. We give the impression of believing wholeheartedly in the tenets of romantic love, and yet know perfectly well that things do not really work that way.

The "one person in the world" worry is groundless. Half the people applying for marriage licenses live within twenty blocks of each other. Young people feel and say, "I know that someday the right person for me will come along." This implies a passive approach to mate seeking that is simply not practiced because it is unrealistic, even for girls. Mate seeking and courtship rely heavily on competition as a sorting device.

Young folks also know the limits of "falling in love." They realize that although they may have a strong attachment for each other in courtship, they probably will be more in love after they have forged other ties of shared responsibilities, adapted to each other's needs, and reared children in marriage.

The "lightning courtship" seems to be another myth. At least two-thirds of American husbands and wives have known each other two or more years before marrying, and only one out of every six or seven serious love relationships eventuates in marriage.

As for "love is blind," most couples are remarkably aware of the defects in the contemplated partner—even to those of dandruff and bad breath.

Romantic love may not be the best way to choose a mate, but it may well be the dominant workable one modern man has. The subtle and fine adjustments required of a maturing marriage cannot be made without some motivation, some continuing force behind the efforts. Modern American partners to marriage are not linked by dowry, property rights, indissoluble law, clanship ties or other great social pressures. Romantic love first draws them into marriage and then becomes the principal holding bond.

Perhaps more effort should be devoted to helping young people choose wisely and less to criticizing, for reasons more romantic than real, the role of romantic love. In the end, no matter how careful we try to be, our choice is only partly governed by conscious reasoning.

Seventy years of social research are yielding some good generalizations about marriage. One that has stood the test of time is summed up in the expression "likes marry likes," for it seems that mates are selected from a "field of eligibles" determined by similarities of race, social class, age, religion, and proximity and availability. Most of us choose from a fairly limited group of people. The real problem is to select the most potentially compatible person within our social reach.

With these cultural similarities assumed, personality needs then become the dominant forces in the choice of partners. Here it seems "opposites attract." That mate is selected who offers the greatest probability of satisfying maximum needs, as the partners act according to a complementary pattern of motives. Although young people are often annoyed by an insightful discussion of the force of unconscious needs, this in no way alters the impact of these needs on decisions.

Studies also show that the degree of understanding and agreement between spouses is related to marital happiness. A high degree of mutual understanding and agreement marks happy marriages; lack of understanding and disagreement characterize a good many unhappy relationships. Couples frequently describe their marital problems in such phrases as, "We just don't understand each other; we don't see things eye to eye." It would seem only common sense that if two parties to a marriage attribute widely different meanings to such concepts as *love, marriage, husband, wife,* and *sexual relations,* their potential for marital stress is likely to be high. Happily married couples, in fact, show a large measure of agreement on the meaning of concepts essential to marriage. This suggests that a probing discussion of these concepts during courtship might be valuable in predicting happiness. At the very least, it should clarify and challenge ideas and roles anticipated in marriage—such as children, birth control, religion, in-laws, the budget.

All considered, then, guidelines to assist with marital choice can probably best be derived from three sources: (1) assessment of personal readiness for marriage; (2) discussion of the factors which influence choice of mate and; (3) discussion of expectations.

personal readiness for marriage

Pressures to marry, both subtle and overt, are so strong that failure to marry may be taken as a sign of personal incompetence. One consequence is that some people marry before they are ready, and repent at leisure. How can one determine readiness?

By the time a person is old enough to marry, a lot of living has gone on which influences his readiness. He is to some degree struggling on the long journey to selfhood on the basis of patterns set in his early family experiences. The journey is marked by conflict between his need to gain enlarged self-awareness, maturity, freedom, and responsibility, and his tendency to remain dependent and cling to the protection of parents or parental substitutes. The way and the age at which this conflict is resolved in good measure determines his readiness for marriage. More specifically, readiness for marriage relates to realistic self-understanding; clearly defined goals, values, interests; the willingness and ability to make decisions; empathy; and autonomy and love.

Self-Understanding

The greatest barrier to self-understanding is an inflated or phantasy concept of self. Whoever contemplates marriage should have a realistic understanding of his abilities and limits, strengths and weaknesses. With this accomplished, he feels more free to express his feelings and needs, and to share himself with other people, particularly a mate. With self-understanding he learns more fully why he behaves as he does, and is more aware of his biases and their influence on his decisions. His perception of events, ideas, and people clears through him; if he does not understand himself, he is unlikely to understand how others relate to him, including his future partner.

One way to judge yourself is to see how others look at you. As Robert Burns said, "O wad some power the giftie gie us/ To see oursels as ithers see us!" See how their impressions of your major strengths and weaknesses compare with your own. Do the same with your convictions, values, and goals. Would you be weak willed and indecisive or vindictive and imposing? If disparity of opinion exists, try to explore it. Self-examination of this sort to dispel false concepts is difficult, but essential to readiness. If you do not understand yourself, should you expect a mate to share the unknown?

Goals, Values, Interests

Knowing what one wants (and needs) is essential to good selection. Readiness for marriage is in part determined by the clarity of one's understanding of his goals, values, and interests, his plans for achieving these, and his discipline and perseverance in following his plans. He should believe in goals which he selects and imposes himself, not those adopted simply because someone said they were good or because they were imposed on him. The degree of his inner strength and integrity will depend on how much he himself knows and believes in the values he lives by.

Choosing goals will necessarily force him to look before and after, not only here and now. This will give him some perspective for viewing problems with objectivity, and for acting in a rational, deliberate manner with regard to them. He can more likely transcend the pressures of the moment and, in preference to a lesser, immediate one, choose a good which is greater but more remote. The same perspective can distinguish insignificant from significant threats to himself and his courtship and can mobilize realistic defenses and actions when necessary.

Perspective, combined with clear and conscious belief in his goals and methods to achieve them, should yield stable patterns of interest and conduct. A choice as serious as that of a marriage partner should be made against a stable background. Otherwise mutual compatibility cannot possibly be estimated.

Judging the seriousness and stability of one's goals, values, and interests is not an easy matter. One test is to ask how stable these have been to the point at which a decision about a mate is to be made. Does the individual have well-defined interests which he enjoys, carries through to completion? Yes? Name them. Or are they outweighed by interests which flit in and out of the picture? Another test is to ask whether the goals are realistic in terms of abilities and possible achievement. This can be discussed with those whose opinion one would respect in such matters, including the potential marriage partner. Seriously held beliefs should be examined in light of probable truths, and exposed to wise, objective, critical appraisal.

Decision Making

The ability to make good decisions is especially important to the process of mate selection, which is often highly influenced by unconscious needs, and emotional and sexual tensions. As indicated earlier, ability and willingness to make decisions depend in good part on the extent to which one maintains a set of internal values. If the values are stable, one will have a framework for evaluating the consequences to himself and others of alternate lines of conduct. He can then make a choice he believes in, and if he believes in something, he has the courage to stand on his own conviction. This is critical in the selection of a mate who may not be the unanimous choice of parents, relatives, and friends, for sometimes efforts are made to shake one's confidence. Here especially the individual must have faith in his decision. He must believe in it strongly enough to judge it by the quality of the decision itself, not by how it is accepted. He should not postpone a judgment of the rightness of his decision until he looks at the audience.

Ability to make good decisions does not come automatically; it is achieved. And it is not achieved in one bound; it is cumulative. Each independent decision enlarges the experience in decision making from which to make a better one next time. Fortunate indeed are the young adults whose parents were wise enough to allow them to reach their own decisions wherever possible. One test of ability to decide is to ask oneself and those whose judgment is respected about the quality of one's decisions up to the point of mate selection —vocation, summer jobs, automobiles, friends, clothing, and so forth.

Empathy

Empathy is the ability to identify with another, to imagine oneself in his place and to make decisions and choices with a view to his feelings as well as our own. Empathy derives in part from a belief in the capacities of people to reason, to feel, and to decide wisely on the basis of values that are understood, accepted, and shared, and from a desire to help people achieve these capacities.

People differ in their ability to interpret the attitudes and intentions of others correctly, and in the accuracy with which they can perceive situations from the other's standpoint, and thus anticipate how they might like the decision to go, or how important it is to the other person. Since marriage has become increasingly democratic, it is important that one partner can consider the views and feelings of the other in reaching the decisions under which both must operate. The degree to which a person possesses the capacity for empathy helps reflect his readiness.

Courtship is a good testing ground for empathy. Are the decisions about joint activities made by two partners or does one decide for both? To what extent does the one deciding for both realize he is doing this and, more importantly, why? Is he condescending in that he indicates *he* is reaching the decision for both because he obviously can do it better? Does the partner agree that he should be making the decision or can do it better? Is he insensitive to the possibility of change in himself or in his position, and does he conclude that only a change in the potential partner will satisfy the situation? If indulged or permitted in courtship, the pattern may be difficult to change in marriage. Unilateral decision making can boost the ego in courtship but becomes wearing when carried over to everyday marital life.

Autonomy and Love

Autonomy is best defined as a composite of most of the characteristics of readiness discussed thus far: the clarity of the individual's conception of himself, the extent to which he maintains a stable set of internal values, the degree to which he is self-directed and self-controlled, his confidence, and his respect for self and for the feelings of others derived from his ability to perceive their feelings, needs, and motivations. Autonomy requires courage, and this is in essence its link to love. It takes courage not only to assert oneself but to give oneself, and to give oneself is love. The autonomous person is sure of himself, can give himself, and thus can love.

Those who call for love loudest often express it least. We receive love not in proportion to our demands or sacrifices or needs, but roughly in proportion to our own capacity to create and give love. Those who yammer for expressions of love in courtship, who feel they are giving more love than they are getting, have not yet learned to love and may not in marriage. Love should be expressed, not learned, in marriage.

Signs of Unreadiness

One sign of unreadiness for marriage is excessive reliance on parents and authorities. The individual is unable to know what he believes, let alone stand up for it, and so looks to someone to make decisions for him. Having no real convictions, he cannot act independently. In this event there is the danger that he may not change after marriage and will continue to depend on his parents, or transfer dependence to his marriage partner. Thus, a husband may expect his wife to support and care for him as his mother did; or a wife may look for another father. Uncertainty and anxiety about an appropriate role in marriage encourages some women to remain dependent. They feel useless and seek to remain attractive by flattering a man's ego through frailty and dependence. They are passive, clinging vines. In short, one-way dependency relationships can be burdensome, boring, and stifling. Parental dependence is a factor in a significantly large number of divorces.

Here and there it is believed that marriage is a cheap and effective form of psychotherapy—"Her problems will take care of themselves once she is married." "All he needs is a wife to look after him." Thus if you are a confirmed homosexual or a chronic alcoholic, if you are lonesome, immature, or depressed, all you need is a willing victim and a wedding license. The outstanding—and most pathetic —example is the woman whose conceit in the power of her love overrides the power of her mind and senses, and who marries the near or established alcoholic, convinced that what he needs is a "good" woman's love. The erroneous assumption is that living in marriage is easier on personality problems than living alone. In general, personality problems should be resolved as fully as possible *before* marriage. This advice applies as well to people with physical infirmities who apparently wish to marry only to get a nursemaid.

Another bad risk is the person of absolutes. There is one correct way to do things—*his*. It is best to marry someone who is at least willing to consider negotiating matters of mutual importance. Rigidity is not a sign of character strength so much as of ossification which leaves the character brittle—if he bends, he breaks.

Other poor marital risks are overly concerned with rights to the neglect of responsibilities. One of these is the young lady who, in seeking advice of a counselor about marrying a certain young man asked, "Who gets the furniture in case we are divorced?"

Finally, no one is ready for marriage who feels he is giving more than he anticipates getting out of it. ("Lucky girl, getting a fellow like me," or vice-versa.) There are no bargains in marriage, except with fair trade.

Few people, if any, are totally ready for marriage in terms of all the standards discussed. Marriage allows for some growth in the achievement of these standards. At the very least, however, the readiness question should prompt persons to anticipate where difficulties might arise and to discuss where premarital adjustments can and should be made.

factors influencing choice of mate

It is evident, as we said earlier, that mates are selected from a "field of eligibles" determined by similarities of race, social class, age, religion, and proximity and availability. Such evidence may be meaningful for society-at-large and for theorists, but it has little value for individuals. What role should some of these relatively objective, impersonal factors play in the choice of a mate?

Physical Factors

Age

Age is a comparatively noncontroversial factor. Relative maturity of those contemplating marriage is more important than chronological age differences. In general, a difference of five years or less seems to be of no great moment. In our culture men generally marry women younger than themselves, probably because their physical and sexual development is slower, and their education and training to earn a living are usually more prolonged. If a man marries a woman older than himself he may find the age difference accentuated when his wife mixes with those wives of his friends who married women younger than themselves.

If the age discrepancy is great, glandular changes and other physiological and psychological aging factors might result in different needs and drives in man and wife. Also, it is well to remember that the male reproductive span is longer. But the question of age differences is usually minor.

Physical Attraction

Physical attraction is a stimulus to the interest of partners in each other, but the definition of physical attractiveness varies greatly. Beauty is in the beholder's eyes. What is ultimately important is mutual attraction regardless of what others might think. However, no one wants a mate he feels like hiding in the closet, or for whom he must apologize. Husbands might extol the virtues of companionship and good cooking, but they may not be completely sincere.

The real caution, however, is to avoid marrying for physical attractiveness alone. Other characteristics have greater bearing on the success of a marriage. The unusually attractive person can be complacent and indisposed to working very hard to make things succeed. Physically attractive people in general find that good things come more easily to them than to their less attractive brethren. Also, the competition to possess physical beauty sexually is high, and one must expect that this will not subside after marriage.

Good grooming, weight control and exercise can do much to improve and maintain physical attractiveness. So can emotional health. As any beautician will confirm, happiness is the main ingredient in facial beauty. What is important also is the desire and effort to maintain good physical appearance. People can adjust to wide inherent differences in physical beauty, but almost everybody objects to sloppiness.

Physical Health

Closely related to beauty is health. Couples should know about each other's physical condition. They should both have physical examinations before marriage and annually thereafter. The physician can answer many important questions: What level of stamina and physical well-being has the individual thus far enjoyed? Is this adequate for the demands of raising a family? If not, what special problems might be imposed? What hereditary diseases, emotional instabilities, or other special conditions appear in the family background, and what are their implications for marriage? Physical infirmities, real or imagined, can be used as a refuge from sexual and other responsibilities in marriage. In the case of the woman, is her state of health such that she can safely anticipate children? Are the sexual reproductive organs apparently functioning normally in both partners, and, if not, what might be the implications? Is there any question of impotence or premature ejaculation in the male, or of frigidity or inability to achieve orgasm in the female? Definitive answers to such questions will not always be forthcoming, and are usually not needed. But even general discussion backed by informed medical opinion will relieve anxieties and provide adequate answers in most major areas of concern.

Few engagements are broken because of the findings of physical examinations, but it is only fair that partners know all they can about each other *before* marriage. If they discover that children are unlikely because of physical deficiencies of one or both—e.g. testicular damage due to mumps in the male, ovulatory problems in the female—they may nevertheless decide to marry. It is far better, however, to face facts beforehand than to experience shock and frustration afterward.

Race

Race is regarded primarily as a physical factor since its most obvious manifestation is physical appearance. In this age of population mobility and extensive travel, interracial marriages are more common, and yet acceptance varies greatly by family, friends, and community. In many places, crossing racial barriers in marriage can place severe handicaps on all concerned. Degree of acceptance can relate to the combination of races—white-black, white-yellow, yellow-black—or to the socioeconomic level of the couple. If partners to an interracial marriage are not accepted socially, their children may suffer stigma by peers.

To make an interracial marriage work, partners have to be that much more resourceful and confident in the bases for their marriage. Racial differences may also bring vast cultural and social differences which have to be bridged, and it is difficult to know when the influence of one stops and the other starts. There is no biological advantage or disadvantage peculiar to interracial marriages. At the very least, persons contemplating interracial marriages should explore as fully as they can the burdens of racial differences, for in this day and age they are sure to be pioneers. They will then have to decide if they and their children should shoulder these frontier burdens.

Sexual Attraction

The biologist considers sexual attraction to be of fundamental significance because it leads to perpetuation of the species. The psychologist finds in the sexual impulse the reservoirs of motivation for many day-to-day activities (including humor and body play—the "light touch") necessary for the success of the marriage. Sociologists recognize the contributions of sex to the stability of the family unit and society and most people appreciate its role in bringing marriage partners to greater fulfillment. There are, alas, always a number of people who view sex (even in marriage and certainly in courtship) as an unfortunate necessity, a degrading weakness of the flesh, something to be done in the dark. These people are sometimes the victims of attitudes imposed on them as children by misguided parents; or religion interpreted by the person to stress the sinfulness of sex is sometimes responsible.

Sex and marriage are irrevocably related. Some regard them as synonymous. When the recent rash of surveys of sexual behavior first revealed the high incidence of extra-marital sex relations, some predicted the end of marriage as an institution.

How important is sex in marriage? Although sexual satisfaction contributes to a total love relationship, sexual inadequacies or differences can be tolerated if the marriage is otherwise good. It has been said that sexual compatibility accounts at best for 20 per cent of marital adjustment, and that it is far more important in the early years of marriage than later. The bean jar story is supposed to be illustrative. If one bean is put into the jar each time sexual intercourse occurs in the first five years of marriage, and one bean is taken out each time intercourse occurs from the sixth year on, the jar will rarely be emptied. In fact, as marriage progresses the couple develops new outlets and bonds—caring for children, running and paying for a household, caring for each other when ill—which bring a gradual acceptance of each other as working partners and parents as well as sexual partners. The diminution in frequency of sexual relations which accompanies this transition is often balanced by enhanced emotional overtones brought to the sexual act by increased regard and respect for one another, which make the sex act a more rewarding emotional experience.

One reason that sexual incompatibility is overrated is the large number of times one hears of it in relation to divorce. It is important to understand that sexual incompatibility does not normally relate to the size of the sexual organs or to vast discrepancies in sex drives, but to some psychological impediment to mutual sexual satisfaction. The impediment usually derives from a host of factors which may not relate to sex specifically, but more to the marriage in general and the personalities of the partners—respect for each other, family finances, conflicting social and recreational activities. Unverbalized or repressed hostility is often expressed through the rejection of or reluctance for sex relations. Because relations are physical and satisfaction or lack of it is easy to judge, they are often made the barometer of happiness in marriage. It is significant that when these other factors are improved, sexual compatibility is also improved.

Sexual attraction and stimulation determine to a considerable extent which girls will be sought after by young men and vice-versa. But once this attraction and stimulation have served their purpose, what is the continuing role of sexual factors in courtship? It may serve to submerge differences in order to create the illusion of reconciling incompatible traits, to sustain the relationship when it seems it might collapse. Many young couples "neck" their way out of problems which arise in courtship. But if sexual attraction is enough to sustain courtship, it is not enough to sustain marriage. Sexual factors become dangerous when they dominate the courtship and prevent the adequate testing of other areas critical for marital happiness. Sexual attraction in itself is helpful, not harmful, but it is potentially damaging when it diverts exploration of other important areas of interaction.

How does one find out about sexual compatibility before marriage? The young man might like sexual relations before marriage as a direct test, but it is not that easy. Aside from the social, moral, and personal restrictions and consequences (discussed under premarital intercourse in Chapter Three) is the fact that the young woman is emotionally slower to develop a positive sexual response. As a rule she requires the trappings of love, security, and social acceptance. And whether she realizes it or not she (more so than the male) regards her sexual organs as primarily for reproduction, which while not incompatible with sexual satisfaction, should not be entirely separated from it. In addition, some young married couples who find their early sexual adjustment satisfactory think that this will apply throughout their marriage. If other areas of their marriage create problems, however, sexual satisfaction diminishes. In short, satisfaction in sexual intercourse before or early in marriage is not a valid predictor of satisfaction throughout marriage.

Courtship with its necking and petting should probably give most couples a reasonably accurate understanding of their potential sexual compatibility, even without engaging in sexual intercourse. At any rate, the attitudes which undergird sex drive and compatibility can usually be developed in a mutually satisfying way in marriage. Few discrepancies exist that cannot be overcome.

Socioeconomic Factors

"She made a good catch," can mean that a girl married someone of a socioeconomic position higher than that of her family. If so, she might also have created some problems affecting the happiness of her marriage. Studies tell us that economic factors (short of extreme poverty) do not significantly influence marital adjustment; nevertheless some authorities are convinced that they do, but nobody really knows how.

Attitudes about money influence motivations considerably. What may seem healthy financial goals and ambitions at the start of a marriage can become avarice later. Undue emphasis on money distorts the capacity to give oneself in love. A healthy respect for money is essential, but we must watch out for those who need it as a source of strength or symbol of their worthiness. Both the spend-thrift and the overly frugal person have limited capacity for the healthy give and take of love. Marriage is primarily an emotional joint bank account, and both partners should make regular deposits. If this account is in good shape, money matters can be resolved reasonably well.

In our culture, social status and income are closely related. Opportunities open to persons of one income are closed to others. One raised in a well-to-do family may have trouble adjusting to a marriage based on more limited means. Giving up things which are commonplace in one environment but luxuries in another may cause some resentment.

Parents of the wealthier spouse sometimes like to help out. They are not patient about financial achievement by the new couple and like to move them as rapidly as possible to their own level—which they reached after thirty years of marriage. Offers of gifts may and perhaps should be resented by the less wealthy spouse. Young marrieds should be prepared to sever parental dependencies, including those that are financial. Readiness for independence in all societies has been the key to the idea of marriageability rather than actual age. In too many cases teenagers have been permitted to expect instant gratification of desires. They have not been condi-tioned by either education or experience to make achievement of material possessions dependent upon hard work. It may be health-ful to their marriage for them to dispose of their obligations with their own resources. About the only reasonable exception short of dire emergency is the parent's helping out with education on a loan basis. This, however, is more a family investment than a gift.

But the real significance of marrying outside one's own socio-economic level is far more pervasive and subtle, and depends on how many levels apart the prospective mates might be. Manners, eating habits, education, sexual habits, recreation, dress—the total way of life—are markedly influenced by whether one is "upper level," "lower level" or somewhere in between. To prevent a mis-alliance, it is recommended that prospective mates make good use of courtship to determine differences between them, and carefully assess their ability to reconcile these, or at least to estimate the influence they will have on happiness in marriage. One way to do this is to spend considerable time with each other's friends and family, and to learn by direct experience in a wide variety of events.

Family

A prospective spouse cannot be isolated from father, mother, brothers, and sisters. To a large extent he is a product of that family, and in view of this it is wise to get to know them. When you pick your husband or wife (and family) you are also choosing half the genetic inheritance of your children. In a number of ways, you marry into a family.

Children imitate the experiences of parents. A person coming from a happy family is likely to be a better marriage prospect. In this regard parents can best teach by precept, by having a happy marriage themselves. Unfortunately, a person from an unhappy family life can make a poor risk, by being so well adjusted to undesirable practices as to continue them in marriage, sometimes without realizing it.

Family behavior patterns are also important, because they suggest the way children of that family will do things. These patterns define behavior under all sorts of circumstances, especially the common occurrences of daily family life. One's own family patterns are those unconsciously expected of the spouse, and emotional temperatures can rise when these are seen differently. In fact, the same phases of life are observed very differently from family to family— walking the dog (or even having one), giving presents, entertaining, the family meals, evening snack, doing the dishes, punishment, holidays, anniversaries, vacations, religious worship, use of leisure time. It is therefore essential to get to know each other's family well during courtship. One should learn their ways and estimate their influence, for while family roles are not acted out much in courtship, they certainly are in marriage.

Education and Interests

Intellectual ability, level of education, and the general intellectual atmosphere that prevailed in the home during the early life of the individual all relate to the satisfactions expected from a close association in marriage. If the couple feels that one of the benefits of marriage is the opportunity to exchange ideas and grow together intellectually, then it is advantageous for them to start from a reasonably similar base. An unsatisfactory and unchallenging situation may well result if one of them possesses vastly superior intellectual abilities, or has enjoyed extended opportunities for intellectual growth. This might come about, for example, where the wife had not gone beyond high school but the husband has finished college and perhaps even done graduate work and, to make matters worse, entered a profession requiring constant learning. However, there are other views on this subject. Some couples openly declare that the husband should have higher intellectual abilities so that he may lead the family. Marriage can be successful where partners come from different educational and intellectual backgrounds, but it is wise for them to discuss the likely effect of these differences. In any event they ought to share the same level of conversational ability to avoid social embarrassment; and they should be reasonably sure that their native intellectual capacities are not so far apart that a child inheriting the capacity of the less able partner would be a disappointment to the more able.

Compatibility of interests, also important to marriage, can be determined only to a limited extent. Basic interest patterns are pretty well set by age seventeen, certainly by twenty-five; and they do not change much as we grow older, for we are less disposed to begin new activities in which we are less skilled than our peers. No one, therefore, should go into marriage expecting to make over his mate's interests to accord with his own. If during courtship one likes to dance and the other doesn't, the odds are that things will continue that way during marriage. See how many interests you share, estimate the compatibility of your separate interests (bowling vs. checkers, boating enthusiast vs. hydrophobe) and try to judge the influence of these on your marriage.

Religion

Each year more persons are marrying outside their religious faiths. Technically any marriage between members of our major religious faiths—Protestant, Catholic, Jewish—is a mixed marriage. In fact, marriage can be mixed on any number of other factors, such as age, race, social class, educational background, but the term commonly refers to a religious mixture.

In the interest of preserving their own identity most religions are against mixed marriage. Some religions even have specific arrangements to insure that identity. For example, the Roman Catholic religion stipulates that both partners sign an agreement before the marriage can take place that (1) the religion of the Catholic partner will not be threatened, and (2) children to the marriage will be raised as Roman Catholics.

Religious differences between a boy and a girl seem very trivial at a school dance or a cocktail party. Even during courtship, reasoned conferences about religious differences may not be conclusive. The emotion of love is riding high, religious observances and education of the children seem remote, and the feeling is that these things can be taken care of when the time comes. But if the courtship progresses seriously, the couple soon discover decisions or compromises which must be made in respect to the wedding, sex behavior, family planning, finances, friendships, and religious holidays and observances. With the birth of the first child, religious differences may become very important in mother-father and in-law relationships. Will the child be baptized? Will he attend religious schools?

But children may not come. People in interfaith marriages apparently realize that children will cause problems. The lower birth rate and higher rate of childlessness among such couples suggests this. A part of the difficulty is caused by a primary function of the family—to pass down the cultural heritage. When parents are of different religions, the family is a cultural mixture, and the child may be torn between the two sides of the family in choosing his religion and philosophy and way of life. If he goes to church with his mother, the question "Why doesn't daddy pray with us?" may not be easy to answer.

The real problem with interfaith marriages is that religion penetrates every phase of our lives. It reveals itself particularly in those intimate aspects of our lives that are fundamental in the marital relationship, and in the rearing of children. And because they are pervasive, religious differences are difficult to talk about in any meaningful way. A couple planning marriage should therefore explore beneath formal church affiliation to determine religious compatibility: what each religion is for or against, and the extent to which it recommends against or simply prohibits; extent of their devoutness to their respective religions; whose church they will go to, if any; their position, that of their own parents, their in-laws, and the positions of their respective religions on birth control, education of children, sexual practices, and other related areas.

Are problems posed by mixed marriages insoluble? Probably not; some couples seem happy. Such marriages sometimes work well when one mate accepts the religion and culture of the other, or when they adopt a liberal religion new to both. But in any case a mixed marriage adds problems.

There are claims that mixed marriages result in disproportionate unhappiness and divorce. Success or failure in marriage is due to many factors and religion is only one. It may be easier to support religious variations if there are not other basic differences. In any case, *all* known religious considerations should be taken into account *before* marriage.

Love

Readiness for marriage is in many ways readiness for love. There is no point in deflating any further the romantic, unrealistic concept of love that so many critics think is operative in mate selection. Its greatest danger is idealization due to what H. L. Mencken called "a state of perceptual anesthesia." We must define more precisely a desirable love relationship, for we advise young people contemplating marriage to be in love above all else.

Some cynics believe that trying to define love is making something out of nothing. Samuel Johnson said, "If you would shut up any man with any woman, so as to make them derive their whole pleasure from each other, they would inevitably fall in love, as it is called, with each other."

A noteworthy feature of love is the many definitions attached to it, few of which agree. In fact it is often hard to believe the same word is being defined, for it has no fixed meaning. Part of the confusion arises from the newness of the concept of love applied to marriage. For much of history woman was lowly—exploited, treated as property, and subjected to many taboos. Marriages were arranged entirely by men; love had little to do with it in any way. Now it is the most acceptable basis for marriage in our society—all the more remarkably because we accept it as such without knowing what it means. Perhaps it would be best to try to describe love as it relates to another person—a prospective mate.

Individuals are equipped to express love in marriage if they can *give* of themselves, if they have a genuine concern and are willing to make sacrifices for each other. There is an implied reciprocity about love—I am capable of loving you and expect you to be capable of loving me; a lack of love in return is rejection. But, no one can give what he doesn't have, and this applies to love. It also implies that it is most difficult for anyone to express love if he has had little or no firsthand experience with it. Has love played a prominent role in the development of the individual—has he or she experienced it in the home? The answer to this question might in part be an indication of readiness for love.

An individual should demonstrate care and concern in his relationships with his partner. This care should have ingredients best illustrated by a mother's love for her child—protecting, nourishing, comforting, sustaining. No assurances would impress us as sincere if we saw her neglect him. The question to ask is "Do you cherish the well-being and happiness of your partner as much as, or more than, you do your own?" Another might be, "Would you measure up to nursing her in poor health?"

A person ready for love will have respect for his partner, but will not be overdependent on her or encourage her to be overdependent on him. He will look upon her as a unique human being with her own inherent abilities and weaknesses. He will be concerned that she grow as suits her best and not in a way that might be more comfortable for him.

Another sign of love derives from close bodily contact. "I thrill to your touch," should not be an idle group of words. Bodily contact should not only stimulate those in love, but it should strengthen them and give them mutual reassurance and encouragement to explore the unknown together. Partners should desire each other sexually, and want children by each other. They ought to feel good with each other, totally comfortable, like the sound of each other's voices, the sight and smell of each other, accept each other as they are without any big plans for overhaul once the marriage is consummated. Essentially love refers to someone who can be accepted and appreciated wholly, without the need for remaking.

They should feel better when they are together. The old adage that love cures everything is partly true. The cure comes from the emergence of certain definable psychological processes that have a constructive effect on the psyche. The ego is reorganized and possessed of new ways to deal more effectively with life.

They should make each other feel important. At one time women were tangibly important—food preparers, clothing makers, breeders, nurses, caretakers of household and farm. Today we are just rich enough to take many of woman's satisfying domestic functions from her and leave her feeling somewhat useless. It is the man's responsibility to seek and develop with her substitute activities and goals to make her legitimately important. Conversely, when a man finds a woman who fills his emotional needs and makes him feel of consequence to her, she seems rare and marvelous to him. We thrive on esteem, and cannot help loving more the one who esteems us.

It is unlikely that prospective mates will fulfill all requirements to their total satisfaction. Love is not an all-or-none phenomenon, nor have even a fraction of its manifestations been covered here; love for another person is a matter of degree, and there are no symptoms (not even those of the "alarm reaction"—palpitations of the heart and weak knees) to prove unmistakably that one has "fallen." At best the discussions and the answers to some of the questions posed here may provide some clues.

In courtship one can only assess the potential for love; to expect more is unrealistic. *Love* may be a strong word to apply to a relatively untested relationship. A marriage ceremony probably marks the beginning of love, not the culmination of it. Love grows as the partners share experiences in marriage. They don't fall in love, they achieve it.

role expectations

Communication is a crucial element in marriage. The plaint of troubled couples that "we don't understand each other" is no mere chance arrangement of words. Talking before marriage about their expectations might be helpful in reducing potential friction. It is best to know in advance where one stands on specific issues. "I think we'll work that out after we get married," is based on the belief that marital adjustment begins with marriage; in truth happy couples generally achieve adjustment in major areas before marriage. The trick in the discussion is not to avoid challenge and conflict, it is to learn to discuss constructively by bringing issues to the surface and by trying to resolve them through reason with respect for each other's feelings. Offending no one and pleasing each other with a nonthreatening front are out of place in courtship. To hear an engaged person say "we never argue about anything" is cause for concern. By defining their expectations as clearly as they can the partners may understand that their daydreams will not all come true, but they may find a realistic substitute that will please them.

Among issues to be brought out, are the concepts regarding the contributions and responsibilities of each partner in the marriage. Should the man be head of the family, the unchallenged leader, the decision maker, the disciplinarian? Should the woman prepare the meals, clean the house, and play a hard-working but recessive family role, otherwise contributing very little to planning and guidance —for example in family financial matters or family intellectual growth?

Marital tension can run high over who should handle the family money and how to use it. How do they feel about installment buying? Should money problems be discussed openly and democratically with equal judgmental responsibility? Or should the husband have complete control of all finances to the extent that the wife is given an allowance and is not consulted about the use of the family income for investments and insurance? Should the husband and wife have joint bank accounts?

Should, in fact, only the wife be domestic in every sense of the word? Or is it possible for the marriage to function such that both people should operate the home and rear the children? Should the wife go further, if she has the ability, and pursue a career or profession, contributing a substantial part of the total family income? If not, how will she be brought to fulfillment? From kindergarten through college the girl is given much the same education as the boy. She is encouraged to compete and excel in the classroom. Can we realistically expect her suddenly to find deep, total fulfillment in taking care of a child, home, mate?

How many children would the partners like to have? Should they be spaced, and if so, what contraceptive measures would be used? What about child rearing attitudes and theories? Which will be used and how tolerant, relaxed, or rigid will they be? And what of sexual satisfaction? How far should partners go in trying to satisfy each other? What are their views on what is natural and unnatural in sexual relations? The answers to these questions should indicate what to expect with regard to many aspects of marriage. Their very personal nature will make them difficult to discuss revealingly, but no less valid.

These questions have been suggestive only. The task before the couple is to identify those things they think vital to their marriage, explore them honestly and thoroughly and seek help with what they cannot answer to their satisfaction.

premarital counseling

There is nothing new about giving advice and assurance to those about to be married. Parents, relatives, friends, teachers, ministers, and the family physician have been doing this for as long as can be remembered. Often, however, the advice is unsolicited and in some cases not very good.

Sometimes prospective marriage partners are seeking only factual information, and the appropriate authority—clergyman, lawyer, physician—can easily give it. In other instances, however, the questions of the couple reflect anxiety about marriage in general and their suitability for each other in particular. Or there may be issues which they cannot resolve to their mutual satisfaction. To handle matters of this nature recourse to specially trained professional help may be desirable.

Many professionals in their everyday work deal with the problems of actual or prospective husbands and wives—physicians (particularly family physicians, gynecologists, and psychiatrists), psychologists, clergymen, social workers, lawyers, and teachers, are examples. By no means are all members of these professions equally well equipped for marriage counseling; yet in each profession will be found some who as a result of interest and training or wide experience are able to deal effectively with marriage problems.

Training standards are becoming increasingly rigorous. Formed in 1943, The American Association of Marriage Counselors is perhaps the best known group concerned with standards. The Association is an interdisciplinary professional organization composed of psychiatrists, gynecologists, general physicians, lawyers, clergy, psychologists, sociologists, social workers, and educators. In order to be considered for full membership in the Association a professional must have, among other qualifications, five years of supervised clinical experience in marriage counseling. Trained and experienced marriage counselors are found in increasing numbers in private practice, in agencies, and as members of interdisciplinary community sponsored counseling teams. This reflects the needs, concern, and interest of the public in building and maintaining healthier and more fulfilling marriages.

A counselor's main job is to create a climate, so to speak, in which the couple feel free to explore the nature of their problems and hopefully gain insight into what may be causing them. With the sources of the problem more fully understood by the prospective partners the counselor can then render further assistance as indicated. He usually finds that the basic requirements for a good marriage are there and will do his best to help the couple overcome their uncertainties and anxieties. As they do so the already strong and healthy aspects of their mutual relationship are even further enhanced. At other times he might allow a couple to expose the inadequacies of their prospective marriage to the extent that they decide to break up. This will be their decision, not his. But it may well be a disillusioning and painful experience for the couple and the families involved, and a thankless one for the counselor. In the long run, however, it will probably be infinitely more satisfactory than encouraging a couple to consummate a marriage which by their own admission is almost sure to fail. If a couple should decide not to go ahead with marriage, a counselor will try to see that they individually get help to overcome any personal deficiencies which might interfere with success in future relationships.

Those wishing help do not always know how to get it. Clergymen, physicians, college or university counseling services, organizations concerned with mental health or family services, and community organizations like the YMCA, are good places to start. A selected list of national organizations at the end of the chapter might prove helpful.

Medical Counseling

Almost all states require health certificates before granting a license to marry. Certification requires of the applicant a physical and genital examination and a blood test for syphilis. Before such a regulation existed, syphilitics were marrying and passing the disease to the spouse and even to the children. When the couple comes in for this examination, the physician has an opportunity to talk about the forthcoming marriage and give them the guidance they so often want but are unable to obtain. He can discuss their general concerns and attitudes about sex, themselves, each other and marriage, examine their pelvic and genital organs, discuss the sex act, and if asked, talk about family planning. He can query them on their plans for marriage, how long they have known each other, their family, religious, and educational backgrounds, and ask if there are any trouble spots—emotional, physical, or family—that they feel may become a problem during the marriage. If they have not read much about marriage, he can give them a short list of publications to choose from.

The couple are then individually examined, and in the privacy of the examining room it is possible to ask questions that could not have been raised before the other person. At this time the physician informs the individual of any findings of an emotional, physical, or organic nature—e.g. sexual fears or inadequacies, sexual and pelvic organs of abnormal function and structure—that may cause trouble for the individual or the marriage. The physician also helps his patient develop a perspective for evaluating the possible effects of these findings.

Examination of the Woman

The woman should have a complete general physical examination. If she has weaknesses of the heart, lungs, kidneys, or blood that may be serious enough to influence pregnancy and caring for a baby, she should be apprised of these (and so should her intended partner). A record should be made of her menstrual history; any irregularities should be discussed, and their effect on childbearing, if any, brought out. An internal pelvic examination of the woman is essential. In some cases, because of an intact hymen, it may be necessary to postpone this examination until shortly after marriage. Ideally, however, it should occur before marriage. In some instances it may be wise to ask the physician to stretch or incise an intact hymen, and thereby make examination easier and minimize the possibility of pain on initial intercourse. Such a procedure is simple and painless. However, an adequate pelvic examination can almost always be made without disturbing the intact hymen.

If the examinations show everything normal, it is reassuring for the woman to hear this from the physician. She should also be told about any irregularities—particularly those which might adversely influence the sex act or pregnancy—vaginal discharge, irritation of the cervix, ovarian dysfunction—and about what remedial action should be taken.

Douches, vaginal and body odors, deodorants, menstrual guards, and so forth, must also be discussed, for anxiety about such matters now runs high under pressure from Madison Avenue. Many women who routinely use douches for what they believe to be hygienic reasons should not be doing so, and some who should use them, do not. The indiscriminate use of the douche, especially the medicated douche, can be more harmful than helpful unless advised by a physician. The vagina normally has bacteria present which are helpful in protecting the membranes from irritation and infection by destructive and disease-causing bacteria. The use of strong or medicated douches can disturb this healthful state and cause trouble. Routine douching for "feminine hygiene" is discouraged; natural processes keep the vaginal tract clean.

Some women feel they should use a douche after intercourse because they feel "sticky" or "messy" and are occasionally aware of the odor of the male semen, and fear that others will notice this odor also. Most of the semen dribbles out of the vagina when she stands or urinates after intercourse. What semen remains in the vagina is usually not acutely malodorous and has no harmful effect on the vaginal membranes. There is especially no reason for using the perfumed douche. It may be harmless when used as instructed, but it is no more efficient for cleanliness, or contraception for that matter, than plain water. Cleansing the external genital organs with mild soap and water is adequate.

Comfortably warm baths and showers are especially desirable during menstruation. The menstrual flow may develop a slight odor, and perspiration glands are busiest at this time. The physician may well wish to discuss menstrual guards. The tampon and the sanitary napkin types have various advantages and disadvantages for particular women depending on circumstances like the amount of menstrual flow and the size of the hymeneal opening. The reason for using a particular type may change with the advent of marriage. For instance, a woman who before marriage could not use a tampon because of a small hymeneal opening, may be able to use one after the hymen has been dilated by intercourse. While the menstrual flow is odorless as it leaves the body, odor may develop once it reaches the air. Menstrual guards have a mild deodorant built into them to minimize this odor. They come in different sizes to accommodate periodic changes in the quantity of menstrual flow for a particular woman, as well as the variation in quantity from woman to woman.

Examination of the Man

The examination of the male is a somewhat simpler matter. He also should have a thorough physical examination. A husband and father has physical responsibilities that he should be equipped to handle. If any impairments are found which might interfere with supporting his family or participating in vigorous family life, these should be brought to his attention. A brief discussion of his sexual history—exposure to venereal disease, sexual difficulties or anxieties —should be followed by an examination of his genitals. If there is any reason for the physician to suspect difficulty with the sex act (such as premature ejaculation, impotence, a tight foreskin) or with fertilization (mumps, atrophy of testes), treatment or further tests might be suggested.

Sexual Intercourse

In the course of the individual examinations, or together afterwards, the couple can be given information to help consummate their initial sexual intercourse without undue difficulty. Some few do not know how to achieve the first sexual union, or they know intellectually but not physically. Charts or other demonstration devices may be useful to the physician as he communicates these details.

A good sex life is important to marriage, and a good sex life is nothing more or less than a mutually satisfying one. There are sometimes misconceptions about a woman's sexual response. There is no biological reason why a woman should not enjoy sexual relations as much as a man. It seems, though, that uncertainties and impressions about her role in sex which have been imparted to her by her culture and family, often make it more difficult for her to be aroused sexually. Even men have an unclear picture of what sort of sexual partner they expect in a wife. They want a wife who is responsive, but not aggressive. They want neither a frigid wife nor one who seems to enjoy intercourse too much.

The sexually overaggressive woman sometimes puts the man on the defensive, and makes it difficult for him to function—almost as if she were challenging him to prove himself. Some men do not really expect a wife to take the sexual initiative except by way of a generally affectionate and loving approach. They resent the wife who initiates genital play. In spite of what a man says, he may still feel that sex is vulgar, and its unbridled expression is not appropriate to the "nice" type of woman.

Time and again, however, the problem is one of restraint or even frigidity in the wife, and this is equally disconcerting to the male. Unreceptiveness, especially because it carries implied rejection, can reduce satisfaction from sexual relations, but frigidity can discourage or preclude them. A frigid wife may suffer a spastic cramp of the vaginal muscles (vaginismus—a rare condition), which prevents entrance of the penis; or tense and tight vaginal muscles may make penetration painful or control of the erect penis difficult, with the result that the male may suffer quick or premature ejaculation. A man may be especially troubled by his wife's frigidity because she looks "sexy" (and in company might even talk that way), and he feels her dissatisfaction or unreceptiveness may be due to some inadequacy in him. This interpretation may in fact be deliberately fostered by the unresponsive woman who wants to cover her own inadequacy. It is important for the physician to make clear that women who look desirable and dress provocatively may not necessarily respond warmly sexually. Women have learned to use sex as a lure but this does not mean they are all emotionally or functionally equipped to enjoy it. The "sexy" looking, but unresponsive woman is rather like the "mirror athlete" who develops his figure for narcissistic glorification and appreciation, but for nothing functional.

If restraint is a problem it is probably because the female has practiced it for twenty years or so and does not suddenly release it, even in marriage—all the more so because she is not sure she should, wants to, or can. The relaxed, accepting attitude of a loving husband eventually may help her to overcome her restraint, but in view of the many cultural influences on sexual adjustment in marriage, it is well to advise both partners against expectations of complete satisfaction in initial and early sex contact. The biological function of sexual intercourse is easily fulfilled, but emotional satisfaction takes time, patience, and mental effort by the partners.

Sexual intercourse, properly performed, consists of three stages: preparation, sex act proper, afterplay.

Preparation. First is the matter of cleanliness of the body; the genitals should be acceptably clean before the sex act begins.

Next is the approach. There is usually some lag in female arousal which the male will have to help overcome. To be a fully cooperative partner a woman should try to experience as much pleasure as possible. This is frequently tied in with a sense of being loved. To assist with this, the man should make certain that sex fore-play with loving overtones is sufficient to help establish the readi-ness of the woman, and that the sex act continues until the woman also achieves an orgasm or derives maximum pleasure. Some women are capable of satisfying sexual relationships without experiencing full or even partial orgasm. But other women with several children have never known any deep pleasure from marital relations and regard sexual experiences as a service to their husbands between pregnancies. It is possible of course for a woman to conceive with-out deriving any pleasure whatsoever from the sex act. Her eroge-nous zones—lips, tongue, breasts (particularly the area around the nipples), inner thighs, labia, vaginal opening, clitoris—should be ex-plored and stimulated. If they receive proper stimulation (gently applied) the desire for insertion of the penis in the vagina is greatly increased. Stimulation of these organs is not only normal, desirable and permissible, but essential. A woman frequently makes the mis-take of thinking that the male should know intuitively what to do to arouse her sexually. It is best if she indicates by word and action the type, quality, and amount of sexual foreplay she wishes so that the husband can be guided. Here is no place for false modesty, em-barrassment, or concern with what is "normal." Any type of prepa-ration the partners consider desirable is permissible. The purpose of foreplay techniques is to permit man and woman to express their deep love and trust in one another. This elevates the meaning of the sex act for them and endows it with spiritual and emotional mean-ing. Outmoded taboos about what is proper and what is not in sex foreplay can unnecessarily detract from sexual pleasure and purpose.

In addition to some erogenous areas which are naturally endowed, other areas can be activitated. Some women respond to a stimulation of areas of the body which cause no response in others. It is important for the partners in a loving relationship to learn where these areas are so that greatest natural pleasure might be derived. This is one reason why sex in a lasting relationship is so much more satisfying than casual or promiscuous relationships. Permanency allows the opportunity to discover and cultivate the most gratifying types of responsiveness.

The couple should make known to each other their readiness for intercourse. Some physical signs appear in the woman. For example, the Glands of Bartholin at the entrance of the vagina secrete a fluid which lubricates the passage in preparation for the penis. This moisture can be felt with the fingers. Nevertheless the couple should communicate their readiness by word.

The *sex act proper* begins with the insertion of the penis into the vagina, and continues as an in-and-out thrusting motion of the male organ with reciprocating pelvic muscle movements by the female, culminating in ejaculation at orgasm by the male. There is always ejaculation but not always adequate satisfaction. In some men, the orgasm may be "so-so" or "dribbling out"; and if this happens often it may be a sign of partial impotence. The condition may be caused or aggravated by too prolonged foreplay, or by overcontrol (delay of orgasm) in an effort to help the woman reach her climax. It may be a case of the husband trying *too* hard to satisfy the wife who is singularly slow to respond.

For the most part, however, the man receives at least some satisfaction each time he achieves orgasm, but he may not be concerned enough with satisfying the woman. It is desirable and even *essential* that some pleasure from the act be experienced by the woman as well. Immediate loss of erection or withdrawal by the male after ejaculation may deprive the woman of inner stimulation for her as yet ungained orgasm. If she fails to derive satisfaction and feels the desire and need for it she should, tactfully, let her partner know this. He can then try to bring her to orgasm by manipulating the clitoris, vagina or other sensitive and responsive organs. In the future, however, he should try to delay his orgasm until the woman can reasonably be expected to derive pleasure. For her part, she should "let herself go" and try to respond without unduly delaying him (and perhaps precipitating the partial impotence described above). It might be unrealistic for a woman to expect orgasm from each sexual experience. In fact it is improbable that both partners will be equally responsive to intercourse *each* time it takes place or that they will achieve mutual *simultaneous* orgasm, the often recommended ideal, very frequently. Nevertheless, intercourse is successful only when both partners receive *some* satisfaction. *It is not enough for the woman to serve the needs of the man.* They must both learn to guide and assist each other to mutual satisfaction. They must let each other know what they are enjoying and responding to, what they would like the other to do, and how far they are from climax.

How does a man know when a woman has an orgasm? More by emotional than by physical manifestations—her tenderness toward him and a certain emotional release in her body and manner. Although a woman can simulate orgasm to reinforce the male ego, her gentle warmth may be somewhat lacking afterwards. More often the fulfillment of her emotional needs, like being physically admired and loved (narcissism) and giving satisfaction to the man, plus some of her own sexual satisfaction will give the woman an emotional release. Orgasm is therefore not always imperative, and the woman has warm and tender feelings for her mate nevertheless.

Afterplay. When the sex act has been completed, the couple should remain in an embrace, perhaps leaving the penis in the vagina. They should show mutual tenderness and convey a feeling of loving each other in a total sense, as well as sexually. Men are sometimes insensitive to the importance of the "afterglow" to the woman. This is the time when the woman draws strength, security, and serenity from the man's love for her.

There are various positions for the sex act. Some may prove more satisfactory than others for a particular couple. The male above, between the separated thighs of the female is the most usual. During the initial explanatory session with the couple, the physician will probably not go into a detailed discussion of a variety of positions, but simply point out to the couple that they should feel free to explore in order to discover those most rewarding for them. Here again there should be little concern for what is "normal." Later on, after some trials and experience on the part of the couple, various positions and their advantages and disadvantages to gratification and pregnancy can be discussed with less risk of overwhelming the couple. The main purpose of the premarital discussion is to prevent unfortunate (and at times traumatic) early experiences with the sex act, which may prejudice or delay the achievement of a successful sexual relationship.

Couples frequently wish to know how much intercourse is normal. The answer might be given that two or three times a week is the norm during the early years of marriage, but the needs of individuals differ and they should honor their own and their partner's in so far as they can. They should at the same time be cautioned about statistics relating to sexual outlets. One value of statistics lies in removing from isolation the individual who thinks he is different; but they tend to emphasize frequency to the neglect of quality. This may encourage some to think that good sexuality is nothing but frequent sexuality. *Good* sexual experiences are not measured by frequency so much as by the ability to give and get satisfaction.

Sexual Incompatibility. Some seem to think that sexual incompatibility arises because of a disproportion in the size of the penis and the vagina, yet this is rarely the cause for incompatibility. Adjustments can be made for most variations in size. Incompatibility is mainly psychological in nature. It is usually accompanied by a general interpersonal incompatibility extending well beyond the sexual area. The reason for the confusion is the difficulty of defining a general incompatibility. Because of the sensitive nature of the emotions involved in sexual relations and their close relation to the love feeling, they quickly mirror problems and tensions that arise in other areas of the relationship. As a consequence, sex relations become the indicator of happiness in marriage. Sometimes the opportunity provided by sexual problems for discussion of general incompatibility is very helpful to the total relationship of those concerned.

Heredity

Usually at some point the couple wishes to know what they may transmit to their children.

Except in rare instances when the mother has an acute illness or infection during pregnancy (e.g., syphilis), no one is born with a disease; and no one directly inherits high blood pressure or cancer or any other disease. The nature of the tissues of which the body is composed are inherited, however, and the tissues of some individuals may be more susceptible to certain diseases than those of others. Certain deformities may also be inherited. Considerable evidence now exists on which diseases and deformities are likely to be fostered by specific sets of hereditary traits. Knowledge of the history of the partners may enable a physician to tell fairly accurately what the chances are for passing along a predisposition to a disease or deformity.

Such predictions, however, should always be tempered. Everyone is born with a certain number of genes whose variety depends entirely on his ancestors. The genes become a mechanism for establishing limitations and potentialities. They may endow someone with a potential life span of ninety years, or with fewer than nine months of intra-uterine life. What is done with that ninety-year potential life—whether it is fully realized or cut short—is dependent partly on will power and partly on environment, opportunity, and chance.

But heredity is significant apart from disease and deformity. The heights or depths that may be reached are determined at the moment one sperm cell penetrates the wall of one egg cell. The genes present in the nuclei of the egg and sperm cell direct the complete elaboration of every part of the body, no matter how large or how small, how apparent or how hidden that part may be. It is often evident that facial contours and general body structure are similar to those of parents, but it is not so evident but not less true that the brains and organs hidden in the chest, abdomen and anywhere else are also similar to those of a parent (or some ancestor). Looking at the prospective couple, the physician may be able to visualize what a child will look like, but this is risky and he knows it. What the couple should understand is that their characteristics, good and bad, are going to be inherited by their children. If intelligence, looks, build, and other qualities are objectionable, they have reason to conclude that they might be not only tolerating things they do not like in a marriage partner, but also placing them in perpetuity.

family planning

Family planning as it is discussed here stresses the mechanical and physiological aspects of how to postpone or prevent an unwanted pregnancy and how to improve the prospects of achieving a pregnancy that is wanted. If a couple asks for such information in premarital counseling, they should be given it.

Contraception

Contraception is prevention of conception during or after sexual intercourse. Contraception is distinct from abortion. Induced abortion is performed to destroy an embryo after it has been created by the union of a sperm and egg. Contraception prevents the union. In general, contraception is not harmful, will not cause disease, and will not prevent a couple from having a baby when they want one.

Practicing contraception is not only a question of individual health or preference. Authorities point with alarm to the accelerating rate of world population growth. Medical discoveries and widespread advances in sanitation have lowered the death rates, but birth rates have not gone down proportionately. It is predicted that if nothing is done about it soon, world overpopulation will be a fact before the end of the century and bring with it an assortment of desperate problems, not the least of which is a totally inadequate food supply. Malthus may well be the most maligned economist of his time.

As sympathetic as we may be to the need for doing something about world population control, this broader use of contraception is not within the scope of this book. Forceful arguments, statistics, and suggestions relating to this problem have been presented elsewhere. Rather, the concern here is for the benefits of conception control as they pertain to the person and the family.

For the newly married couple, contraceptives might be employed with benefit during that early period of adjustment when they get to know each other, so that early pregnancy and childbirth do not intrude on the things they can do or the places they can go together. The couple might also wish to complete their education, or to work for a period of time to be better able to afford children.

Or there may be medical indications for contraception because of the health of the wife, or, more rarely, because of hereditary conditions with high potential for adversely influencing a child.

Unrestricted fertility in some cases endangers the health of the mother. A twenty-month to two-year interval between pregnancies is desirable so the mother can regain her strength, health and emotional well-being; she needs a respite from the demands of pregnancy and early infant care. This interval is desirable for the newborn child as well. A mother's good health and attention should be ready for the heavy demands made by the new baby during the important first two years of life. Women used to try to achieve this period of grace by prolonged nursing of the baby. During nursing, the breasts produce a hormone which delays ovulation—a good example of nature's protecting the health of the organism.

The health of the next child may be endangered if the interval is too short. Some cases of pregnancy wastage and infant mortality are traceable to the weakened condition of the systems and organs of the mother.

The blessing of children may become a burden when they are too many or chronologically too close. Family life may be impaired and opportunities for education restricted. Most responsible parents want to have the number of children they can bring up with a reasonable chance for growth of each according to his abilities. In some cases economic or other family worries may be so severe that additional children would be a threat to the mental and physical health of the family.

But whatever the reason for it, birth control has long been in the history of man. Records for suggestions about birth control go back about 4,000 years; the earliest means were infanticide and abortion. But even contraception was not invented recently. A version of a condom was described in print over 400 years ago. Contraception was probably first attempted when man became sophisticated enough to understand the connection between intercourse and pregnancy; without other knowledge, it must have been difficult to relate an act occurring nine months before to the birth of a child.

All sorts of contraceptive measures have been tried: withdrawal, inserting cotton plugs dipped in solutions of herbs or roots into the vagina, abstinence around ovulation ("rhythm" or "safe period" method), mechanical barriers like condoms, diaphragms, cervical caps, and uterine plugs, and, recently, a pill which suppresses ovulation. The first attempts at control were crude and largely ineffective. But even today most methods leave something to be desired. Fortunately the high present-day interest in contraception and the increasing financial support for research in the physiology of human reproduction and in population control should bring us closer to the ideal contraceptive—harmless, reliable, free of objectionable side reactions, inexpensive, simple to use, reversible in effect so that a couple can conceive when they stop using it, not interfering with the act or pleasure of intercourse. How do some of the common current techniques measure up?

Diaphragm

The contraceptive technique most frequently prescribed by physicians and family planning centers is the diaphragm with contraceptive cream or jelly. It is used by about a third of the couples of childbearing age who attempt control, and is one of the most reliable methods. The diaphragm is made of soft rubber in the shape of a shallow cup, usually with a flexible metal spring or coil forming the circular outer edge. It works by imposing a mechanical barrier between the egg and the sperm, covering the cervix of the uterus so that the sperm cannot enter. When it is used as recommended, with a contraceptive cream, a chemical barrier is added. The cream also fills the folds in the wall of the vagina upon which the diaphragm rests, thus helping to prevent sperm from getting around it.

The diaphragm is designed to fit snugly between the back wall of the vagina and the pubic bone, the distance of which varies from woman to woman. The device comes in a variety of sizes so that most women can be fitted. If the size is wrong, the likelihood of failure is increased—it may slip during intercourse, or sperm cells might get around the edges. Because of the precise nature of the fit, diaphragms should be fitted by a physician trained in the practice, and sold only on prescription.

Most young women when first instructed in the use of the diaphragm do not like the idea of an examination by the physician for proper fitting, nor the insertion of their own fingers far into the vagina to feel the position of the diaphragm and to determine whether it is covering the cervix. Neither do they like the messi-

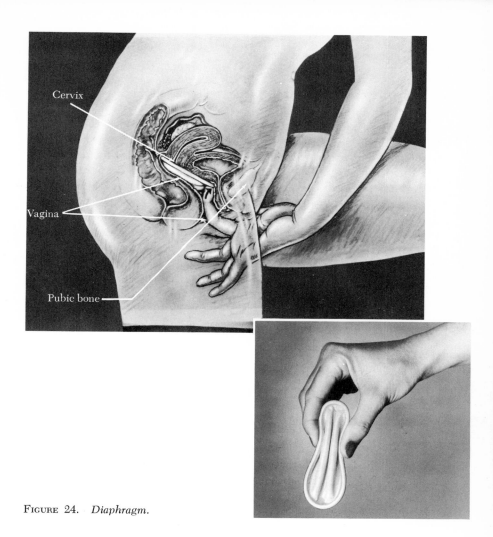

Cervix

Vagina

Pubic bone

FIGURE 24. *Diaphragm.*

ness of the use of cream or jelly. Most of them eventually overcome
these objections, and learn quite easily to insert the diaphragm
properly with their fingers; some, however, prefer a mechanical in-
serter specifically designed for this task. Either way, the diaphragm
is pushed back as far into the vagina as possible, and the forward
rim is pushed behind the pubic bone. When the diaphragm is properly fitted and inserted, neither the man nor the woman should feel
it during the sex act; it is well out of the way. The woman should
not feel it at other times either, nor does it interfere with usual
bodily activities like bladder and bowel functioning.

After the fitting the physician will give the woman general instructions on its use:

1. With about a teaspoon of cream or jelly smear the rim and the cup side of the diaphragm that is to go against the cervix. Insert the diaphragm well ahead of time, perhaps before retiring or anticipated contact, not at the last moment. It may be inserted anytime up to four hours before intercourse, but before having intercourse check to insure that it is properly situated between the wall of the vagina and pubic bone. On some occasions the diaphragm may be inserted when intercourse does not take place; better that than vice-versa. It may seem that the spontaneity of the act is lost when it has to be anticipated so far ahead, or that husbands will resent this anticipation as being too aggressive. Difficulties like this are easily overcome. With time, couples learn to pick up clues from each other as to whether intercourse is going to take place. But if spontaneous arousal occurs, and the diaphragm is not in place, it should be inserted before foreplay has progressed very far.

2. Leave the diaphragm in place at least eight hours after intercourse, which ordinarily means removal the following morning. By that time all of the sperm cells trapped in the vagina should be incapable of fertilization. If relations are desired the following morning, the diaphragm should be removed, contraceptive jelly or cream added, and reinserted.

In addition to making sure these instructions are understood, the physician then supervises several rehearsals of the insertion and removal procedures. It is to be emphasized that the diaphragm will not work properly unless it is well-fitted and the woman knows how to use it.

A diaphragm properly washed, powdered, and stored in its case after each use should last about two years. However, since the vagina is stretched by childbirth, the fit of the diaphragm should be checked by a physician before sex relations are resumed after childbirth. A recheck is also advised following the honeymoon for women who have had no previous sexual intercourse. Because it is not easy (and frequently not possible) to be fitted for a diaphragm with an intact hymen, women about to be married are sometimes advised to use another contraceptive technique early in marriage and are fitted with a diaphragm later. Customarily this temporary alternate technique is the condom.

Condom

The condom is the most popular contraceptive. About 750,-
000,000 are produced in the United States each year. In addition to
being used extensively by married couples, they are by far the most
popular contraceptive employed in extramarital relations. They are
effective, simple to use, harmless, easy to buy, and no special help
from a physician is needed to use them effectively. They can also
help guard against the transmission of venereal disease. In fact they

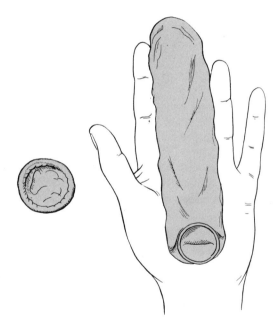

FIGURE 25. *Condom.*

are probably as well known for prophylaxis as for contraception,
which is why they are allowed to be sold so widely, for some state
laws forbid the sale of contraceptives, but not of prophylactics.

Condoms are thin, strong rubber sheaths, shaped much like the
finger of a glove to fit over an erect penis. At the open end there
is an elastic rubber ring which grips the penis much in the manner

of a small rubber band and helps to keep the condom on during intercourse.

Properly used, the condom is among the most effective contraceptives available. The more common causes of failure are bursting and mishandling but most condoms are now manufactured under careful supervision and danger of bursting due to production defects has been reduced.

The condom should be rolled onto the erect penis previous to the initial insertion into the vagina. This will prevent any sperm cells which may happen to be present in the pre-ejaculatory fluid from accomplishing fertilization. On some condoms, a small pocket may be at the closed end. This is to prevent rupture of the condom due to the pressure of the ejaculate, and to accommodate the stretching of the condom during the forth and back motions of intercourse. If such a pocket is not provided it is wise to leave some space at the tip to serve these functions.

The condom is made to fit the erect penis. Immediately after the male climax, before erection is lost, the penis should be withdrawn from the vagina while the ring at the top of the condom is held to prevent the condom from slipping off.

As a contraceptive measure in marriage, the condom leaves much to be desired. It acts as a sensory barrier by precluding the direct contact of the membranes of the penis and vagina. It can at times be irritating to the penile and vaginal membranes, particularly if lubrication in the vagina is scant. Some condoms come slightly lubricated to reduce this irritation. Otherwise it might be wise to add a bit of lubricant to the outside of the condom.

The condom may also introduce some psychological barriers to enjoyment of the sex act. For example, some of the pleasure comes from leaving the penis in the vagina for a time after climax while the partners enjoy each other's embrace. This, of course, is not recommended with the condom. Some men (and most gynecologists) feel that the woman should be in control of the contraceptive technique since she is exposed to pregnancy if it fails. But some women object to any method for which they must assume control (especially diaphragm and jelly) and insist that their husbands use a condom. This may arouse antagonism in him, with a disturbing effect on sexual satisfaction that sometimes carries over to other areas of married life as well.

Moreover if the husband is indifferent, careless, or intoxicated, he may cause an unwanted pregnancy. Everything considered, contraceptive techniques that are the direct responsibility of the wife are preferred by most couples. Besides the condom, withdrawal is the only other common contraceptive technique controlled by the male.

Withdrawal

Withdrawal of the penis from the vagina just before ejaculation so that the semen is deposited outside the reproductive tract is probably one of the oldest contraceptive techniques. To its advantage, withdrawal costs nothing and can always be practiced. While some persons seem to be happy with it, there are disadvantages.

Withdrawal is not as safe or desirable as is commonly thought. It is not safe because the penis may be withdrawn too late, particularly by the young, sexually inexperienced male, or sperm cells may be present in the pre-ejaculatory fluid. It may be emotionally disturbing and frustrating to the male to be concerned with split-second timing while he is trying to enjoy the sex act. The woman may also be worried about the timing, but even when accomplished successfully, the sudden withdrawal may leave her with a pronounced sense of emptiness and incompletion. For long-range satisfaction it is imperative that both partners achieve pleasure from the act—otherwise there will be a cumulative destructive effect. Also, as with the condom, there is no opportunity for a lover's embrace, with penis resting in vagina following intercourse.

Most women prefer a technique for which they are responsible and which allows the sex act to be carried to completion. Besides the diaphragm and cream or jelly, there are effective chemical spermicides.

Chemical Spermicides

The creams and jellies contain chemicals which immobilize or destroy the sperm. Shortly before intercourse, a specified amount of the substance is inserted with an applicator deep into the vagina, in front of the cervix. It will spread over and cover the opening of the cervix and thus act as a chemical as well as a mechanical barrier to the sperm.

Foam tablets and creams also contain agents which destroy the sperm. A tablet is placed deep into the vagina not more than an hour or less than a few minutes before intercourse, to insure that adequate foaming action is still present or has begun. It dissolves and releases a harmless gas to produce a rich foam which covers the cervix. Normally the moisture of the vagina is enough to activate the tablet, but it is a good idea to moisten the tablet with water or saliva before inserting it to make sure it is working properly, or in the event the moisture in the vagina is scant. Foam creams are packaged like foam shaving cream and are applied with inserters so as to cover the cervix. They seem to work somewhat better than regular spermicidal creams.

Chemical spermicides are harmless, but some women find them slightly irritating to the membranes of the vagina and cervix, and others find them somewhat annoying, particularly those with foaming action. Women using spermicides should not wash or douche the vagina before four to six hours after intercourse. Otherwise they may wash away the chemical and mechanical protection of these methods while active sperm cells are still near the cervix.

Spermicidal creams, jellies and tablets are not as effective as the diaphragm with cream or jelly. But some couples find them satisfactory, especially where the woman does not like a diaphragm or cannot use it. It is in their favor that spermicides are easy to get and simple to use. No special examination by a physician is needed, and they can be purchased along with full instructions for use without a prescription at drug stores. It should be remembered that a simple method used regularly may be more effective in the long run than a more reliable method used irregularly.

Douches

Douching for contraceptive purposes consists of flushing out the vagina with water or some other liquid immediately after intercourse in an effort to wash out the semen. Adding chemicals (vinegar, salt, or the like) to a douche does not make it more effective since the main action is mechanical, not chemical. Besides, ordinary tap water is spermicidal and is generally available more easily and faster.

The key to effectiveness of the douche is haste; within ninety seconds after intercourse sperm are within the cervix where they cannot be reached. This places a heavy responsibility on the woman. If she waits beyond ninety seconds, about all she can expect from douching is a decrease in the number of sperm cells which might ultimately reach her reproductive tract—and this may be only a small factor in reducing the possibility of conception.

Douching is the least effective contraceptive technique in common use. (In the few cases in which women have used the douche for long periods with apparent success, one wonders if they would have conceived in the absence of precautions.) Douching allows no postcoital relaxation; one can sympathize with the woman bracing herself for the ninety-second dash. But it is inexpensive and simple. Perhaps it is these factors that make it popular outside the United States. The bidet, common abroad, is a special sink with an upward geyser of water that enables a woman to douche and wash her genitals.

The contraceptive techniques discussed so far depend upon mechanical or chemical means to prevent the sperm from reaching the egg. There are two other techniques, one based on knowledge of the time of ovulation, and the other on suppression of ovulation. These methods are commonly called rhythm and "the pill," respectively.

Rhythm

The rhythm or "safe period" method is based on the biological fact that a woman usually can become pregnant only during that period of her menstrual cycle close to ovulation.

It is now generally assumed that a woman produces only one egg cell during a menstrual cycle. The egg is released from the ovary about fourteen days before the beginning of the next expected menstrual flow and its life span—that is, the time during which it can be fertilized by a sperm cell—is less than twenty-four hours. The sperm cells in turn, if they reach the Fallopian tubes, retain their ability to fertilize the egg for a usual maximum of forty-eight to seventy-two hours. Conception can therefore occur only when sexual intercourse takes place during the few days around the time of ovulation. Presumably, during the other days of the month a woman cannot become pregnant. Conception can therefore be prevented by avoiding intercourse during the fertile days of the cycle.

The problem is to figure out the approximate day of ovulation. Some women are able to tell when they are about to or are ovulating. They experience a little discomfort in one side of the pelvis depending on which ovary is ovulating that month. This pain is termed "mittelschmerz" because it occurs as a rule in the middle of a cycle. Occasionally if it persists and is severe on the right side, it can be mistaken for appendicitis. At the time of ovulation some women may notice a discharge of a small mucus plug or increased secretion of mucus from the cervix. This is explained by the fact that at the time of ovulation the mucus plug of the cervix softens and the secretion of mucus increases to provide more favorable environment for sperm cells to travel to the Fallopian tubes.

But at present, for most women, there is no entirely satisfactory way of predicting the exact time of ovulation. Prediction is based in large measure on a record of the woman's menstrual cycle, but the time of ovulation can also be determined with some accuracy by a record of her daily temperature. If taken daily, immediately upon awakening, the temperature will show a one-half to one degree rise about the time when ovulation takes place and will remain higher for the rest of the cycle. If menstrual and temperature records are kept carefully for several months, and if the menstrual cycles are regular, it is possible to make a reasonable estimate of the fertile and unfertile days.

A woman with a regular twenty-eight-day cycle will ovulate around the fourteenth day from the first day of her period. Allowing four days before and after ovulation to include the time when both the egg and the sperm might remain alive, the fertile or "unsafe" days would last from about the tenth to the eighteenth day from the beginning of her period. From the eighteenth day on there would be no egg present (for it has presumably lived out its brief and unfertilized life in the tube), and conception could not take place. The days before the tenth day are also believed to be safe, but this is much less certain because the length of time the sperm cells can remain alive within the female reproductive system is not definitely known. In addition, if ovulation occurs out of time, and

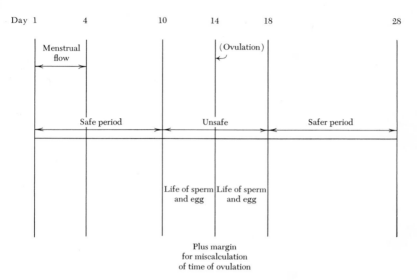

Day 1   4   10   14   18   28

Menstrual flow

(Ovulation)

Safe period   Unsafe   Safer period

Life of sperm and egg | Life of sperm and egg

Plus margin
for miscalculation
of time of ovulation

FIGURE 26.   *Twenty-eight day menstrual cycle.*

it sometimes does, this may happen earlier. All considered, the last ten days are felt to be the safer of the two so-called "safe" periods. To illustrate again, let us consider a woman with a thirty-five-day menstrual cycle. Menstruation will still begin about fourteen days after the egg is released from the ovary. This is generally true of a cycle of any length. Thus, in a thirty-five-day cycle ovulation would take place somewhere about the twenty-first day; by adding four days before and after day twenty-one (possible life of sperm and egg) one can calculate the probable fertile period and abstain. The preceding seventeen days of the cycle—days one through seventeen— are "safe" as are days twenty-five to thirty-five.

If the woman's periods are irregular, the safe and unsafe days will likewise be irregular and therefore unknown. Illness, shock, or other physical or emotional changes can also disturb the menstrual cycle and upset the calculation of the time of ovulation. During World War II accurate records were kept of the menstrual cycles of woman in concentration camps; great fluctuations in these were noted when the women received unpleasant news. It has also been shown that a disproportionately large number of rape cases

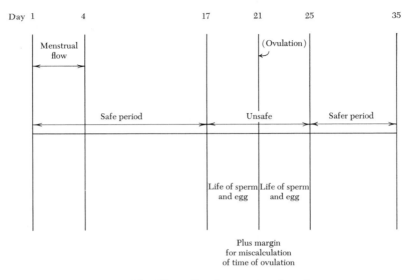

FIGURE 27.   *Thirty-five day menstrual cycle.*

result in pregnancy even though the rape takes place at a time apparently far removed from the expected time of ovulation. And much to the chagrin of brides who have planned to avoid it, menstrual flow can "postpone" the honeymoon. Also, it is not too unusual for a woman to ovulate more than once in a given cycle at some time during her reproductive years.

For these reasons the rhythm method is not entirely reliable or suitable for all women. If it is to be followed, one should consult a physician trained in calculating the safe period. And, of course, even if the period can be determined correctly, the method still places a restriction on intercourse during a large part of the cycle— a fact which does not sit well with all people. Research is in progress to develop simple and reliable home tests for determining more accurately when ovulation takes place. None has yet emerged, but it is to be hoped that some more accurate method can be found, particularly because this is the only control acceptable under some circumstances to a number of religious organizations, especially the Roman Catholic Church.

"The Pill"

A fairly recent development in the search for the ideal contraceptive is "the pill." The pill, taken orally, contains some progesterone and a little estrogen, hormones that suppress the follicle stimulating hormone (FSH) of the anterior lobe of the pituitary gland and thus prevent the ripening of the egg in the ovary. The procedure is for the woman to take a pill every day for twenty days, beginning the fifth day after the start of the menstrual flow. She then stops taking the pill, and one to three days later her menstrual period begins. The flow may be somewhat scantier and of shorter duration than when she is not using the pill.

The same procedure is followed again, beginning five days after the start of the flow. This routine has to be followed *exactly*, for if even one day is missed, ovulation can take place and pregnancy might occur. If she forgets to take the pill one day, a woman should use another contraceptive technique for the remainder of that cycle.

If she wishes to become pregnant, she stops taking the pill. Ovulation usually recurs in the next cycle, and her normal level of fertility is restored. The pill seems to have no direct effect on sexual desire, though some women claim to feel an increase.

The pill is a new method of contraception, and numerous field tests of its effectiveness, side effects, and possible dangers, have been conducted. The results of some of these tests indicate that the pill is remarkably effective and safe. The slight side effects suffered by some women can ordinarily be overcome if the pill is taken for several cycles. However, because it is still being tested, the pill can be purchased only by prescription, and should be taken only under a physician's direction. Until the findings of long-term studies suggest otherwise, the use of the pill as a contraceptive should be limited to three to four years. It is usually not recommended right after childbirth for a woman who wishes to nurse her child, as the pills may suppress the production of milk.

Several brands of the pill are now being sold commercially, but they are financially out of reach of many potential users (about two to three dollars a month), particularly in the underdeveloped countries where it probably could be used to greatest advantage. Price will be reduced in time with increasing sales and cheaper production and distribution costs. As the findings of field tests come in it is also likely that the need for medical supervision, one costly item, will diminish.

When to Use Contraceptives

Many factors help to decide when contraceptive techniques should be used in marriage.

Certainly they should be employed when there are indications that a pregnancy runs the risk of being unhealthful for the mother or the child, or when family worries are so severe that another child would be a threat to the well-being of all. But few cases are so clear. Sometimes the couple needs help with the decision.

The medical considerations and risks of a pregnancy or in delaying one can usually be assessed with the help of a medical counselor. Devout couples should learn all they can about the position of their religion on contraception from the appropriate religious counselors and sources. Help in the economics of family life can be obtained from suitable advisers.

Economic criteria for contraception can be especially slippery. The balance between having a child when conditions are financially right, and planning too conservatively and too long is difficult to determine. Unfortunately some couples wait so long that they deny themselves the children they will want later on.

If contraception has a built-in danger it is that fertility decreases with age, and the prolonged use of contraceptives may place attempts at conception beyond the age of highest fertility. Youth is the greatest ally to fertility. On the average, fertility of both men and women is highest in their twenties.

Another danger of contraception is that the couple may wait so long that they no longer have the physical stamina to enjoy a child. Or, in some cases postponement leads to a total dependency of the couple on each other for the fulfillment of their needs, and the late child unfortunately may be regarded as an intruder.

But after all the information and advice is in, the couple themselves must weigh all of the factors and decide. No one should attempt to make this decision for them.

Summary

The ideal contraceptive has not yet been developed; all have some drawbacks. All the contraceptive techniques currently in wide use, with the possible exception of the "pill," permit neither spontaneity nor are they simple and without mess. But if one wishes the pleasures of sexual relations without the responsibilities of pregnancy, some sacrifices must be made and some discipline exercised. No contraceptive is guaranteed.

Reliability is very much related to motivation and practicality. For example abstinence would be a most reliable contraceptive technique; but it is too much to expect of most couples. In order to avoid the temptation of sexual embrace they would have to keep their physical contacts to a minimum by not being with each other and not sleeping with each other. These avoidances would probably be troublesome to their total relationship. Abstinence is therefore impractical and undesirable.

All things considered, the most reliable contraceptive for a particular couple is the one they are most likely to use consistently, for the major source of failure is lack of motivation with consequent irregularity of use. Any contraceptive will work better than none.

Although some persons wish to avoid conception, others wish to achieve it and find themselves temporarily or permanently unable. The temporary condition is called infertility; the permanent one is sterility.

Infertility

A female is sterile, in the narrow sense of the term, if she fails to produce a mature egg during her reproductive epoch; a male is sterile if he fails to produce a sperm cell during his. These conditions are generally due to inherited or congenital malformations, to total absence or atrophy of the testes or ovaries. Another cause may be occluded vas deferentes or Fallopian tubes. At the present time treatment for most of these conditions is limited, and it is unlikely that they can be corrected. Happily, however, they apply to few of those who wish children.

Impotence

Sterility is often confused with impotence. Sterility can be due to any of the conditions listed above. Impotence is a psychological condition in which the male cannot maintain an erection long enough to engage successfully in intercourse. In the woman, impotence is a spasm of her vaginal muscles (*vaginismus*) which precludes the entry of the penis—a rare condition—or the inability to permit herself to engage in successful copulation (*frigidity*), which happens more frequently. Impotence describes not the inability to produce sperm and egg cells, but rather the failure of the genitals to unite for successful copulation. In this way impotence can be a cause of infertility in the male. Of course, frigidity in the female does not necessarily preclude conception.

Extent of Infertility

It is difficult to judge the extent of infertility, but a proper guide might be the record of couples who use no preventives to avoid pregnancy. About 33 per cent will achieve pregnancy the first month, 25 per cent the second month, with decreasing percentages the following months until after one year there is a residue of so-called infertile couples. Of these about one-third will eventually conceive, and there is left a group of 10 per cent of the original group who will not. Such couples usually wait about two or three years before consulting a physician; they should be encouraged to seek help after a year has gone by.

Causes of Infertility

Human fertility requires normal organs, coordinated glandular function, and a sound regulatory nervous mechanism. Deficiencies in one or more of these components produce infertility. An example of such deficiency is impaired or irregular egg or sperm production that may be due to disease, nutritional insufficiency, glandular (endocrine) disturbances, or emotional factors affecting the function of the reproductive organs. During stress the sex glands become less active in proportion to the increased activities of the adrenals.

Emotions also can be responsible for impotence, spasms of the Fallopian tubes, or an unconscious rejection of pregnancy which in some way inhibits the ability of the individual to achieve it. A woman may fear the birth process for a number of unconscious reasons. She may feel that having a child would place her in competition with her own mother, with dangerous consequences. She may feel that she is not mature enough to take responsibility for a child, or she may dislike infants because of traumatic experiences with younger siblings. In men under stress, sexual urge and sperm cell formation are diminished. In fact, at least one-fourth of all infertility is attributed to emotional factors. When the emotional problems are treated and the tensions eased, a high percentage of the couples achieve pregnancy. An interesting illustration of the effect of psychological factors is that a small fraction of the couples who go to fertility clinics conceive before anything is done for them.

But infertility is a complex matter. Unless he has evidence of absolute sterility in one partner in an involuntarily childless marriage, the physician does not talk of the infertile husband or wife, but of the infertile couple. Rarely is there just one factor for which the husband or wife is solely responsible. Husband and wife must be treated as a unit almost always. The degree of fertility can be evaluated only on the basis of the combined fertility factors. Within reasonable limits one mate can make up for the lower fertility of the other.

The lot of the barren woman has never been a happy one—in primitive societies she was hated and often barred or forced to suicide. Until recently (and in some rural communities, it still applies) lack of offspring when the family was the only source of unpaid labor was a gross economic misfortune. Throughout history, the burden of barrenness has been assumed by the wife. Unfortunately, even today, a large number of wives are subjected to tests and examinations without a first attempt being made to seek the causative factor in the husband. This happens in spite of the fact that the husband is solely or partly responsible in about half the cases of involuntary childlessness in which some abnormality is found.

The woman is troubled not only by her own inability to fulfill her reproductive role but also by her feeling of responsibility for denying her husband a family. It should not be assumed, however, that the husband is unemotional about a childless marriage. Even if he is busy enough and tired enough to be tolerant of his wife's infertility, his own inability to procreate may signify to him loss of manhood or status, and create tensions with in-laws interested in grandchildren. Like the sterile woman, he often becomes overly sensitive and morose. He may be highly susceptible to innuendos and fear the ridicule of his relatives and associates; he may worry about the effect of childlessness upon his wife; and he may wonder if his childless home will always be a happy or even a permanent one.

Premarital Fertility Examinations

In view of all the emotional strains of wanting children and not being able to have them, it seems only sensible to make some simple fertility assessments a part of the premarital medical examination. A minimum requirement would be an examination of the man's semen, and a medical history and careful pelvic examination of the woman; both examinations could be completed at the time of the required premarital blood tests. The examinations would not disclose all the possibilities of infertility, nor, if favorable, would they insure that the couple will have children. But they would provide some basis for appraisal of the chances, and might expose difficulties which could be corrected. If the conditions can be remedied, so much the better, but if not, and if children are very much wanted, the couple may decide not to marry. On the other hand, they may, and usually do, decide to go ahead with the marriage in full knowledge of the prospects, which is far better than having the fact of sterility or infertility come as an unanticipated problem.

The man is usually examined first because he is easier to test. After a general examination of the sex organs, a sample of the male semen is studied for sperm content and general composition. There should be two to four cubic centimeters of semen with an acid-alkaline balance of pH 7.4. It should contain 60–100,000,000 sperm cells per cubic centimeter of which 75 per cent are oval shaped and 60 per cent are active. In every specimen of ejaculate there are some abnormal sperm cells that have poor structure or motility. So long as these do not exceed 25 per cent of the total, the specimen is within normal limits. If it is not, efforts can be made to correct deficiencies through improvement of general health or the functioning of a particular gland or organ. If no sperm cells at all appear, further tests are conducted. The male may be producing no sperm cells, or there may be a barrier between production and delivery.

The examination of the woman is more complex. There are several requisites for fertility in women: normal egg production, unobstructed mechanism for pick-up of egg by Fallopian tube, normal access to the egg by the sperm, unobstructed descent of the fertilized egg into the uterus, a prepared and receptive lining in the uterus, and successful implantation of the fertilized egg in the lining. But usually all the physician will do in a premarital fertility examination is check the history of the woman's menstrual cycle to determine whether ovulation seems normal and whether her pelvic organs appear to be normal. If indications seem unfavorable he can make further checks on her ovulation by keeping records of her body temperature, test to see if her Fallopian tubes are open and whether there are special conditions in her reproductive tract which may block or inhibit sperm cells. These tests are usually given at a later time should childlessness continue.

The physician will then discuss with the couple the normalcy of their condition, or the factors which may interfere with their fertility, and how these factors should be remedied. Within the last few decades the causes of infertility have been receiving serious study—new diagnostic techniques, new treatments, new drugs are being utilized. Couples who a few years ago might have been considered permanently barren can today be helped to have children and fulfill their family aspirations. In about half of the cases that come to clinics, some help can be given.

A knowledge of the menstrual cycle can help couples to achieve conception. Some people who wish children unwittingly concentrate their sexual activity at times when conception is unlikely. If they understand when conception usually takes place, they may see to it that relations occur at those times. This does not mean that couples should save up their relations for these periods. The ability to conceive seems to be enhanced when relations take place regularly throughout the cycle, not just at the time ovulation is assumed to have occurred.

Women of relatively low sexual desire may have their greatest urge for relations immediately before and immediately after menstruation when conception is least likely to take place, since no egg will be present in the female reproductive tract. With knowledge, they can alter their sexual patterns to make conception more likely.

But nature does cooperate in some ways toward the end of conception in that during ovulation a change takes place in the mucus of the cervical canal which improves the sperms' chances for reaching the egg. The rest of the month it is filled with mucus that is thicker and less penetrable by sperm cells. But during the four or five days surrounding ovulation the mucus becomes thinner, more copious, and penetrable.

Artificial Insemination

Artificial insemination is connected with infertility. If a wife has been found fertile and a husband sterile without remedy, or if the husband's fertile sperm cannot be delivered in intercourse, conception may be brought about by artificial insemination. The procedure entails the artificial introduction of semen into the cervix, causing the woman to become pregnant. Although apparently sound in theory it can encounter problems in practice, and conception does not always occur. It has, however, been successful in a high enough percentage of cases so that the procedure is widely used and has contributed to the family needs and happiness of carefully selected couples.

Depending on conditions, the ejaculate containing the sperm may be obtained from the husband or from a donor; preferably the husband. But donor insemination, if the husband cannot produce healthy (*fecund*) sperm, offers real advantages as an alternate to childlessness or even to adoption: the wife and the husband can experience the pregnancy and delivery; the child is in part the wife's offspring and will inherit characteristics from her. But so many factors are present—religious, legal, moral, psychological, physiological—that any couple considering this approach to pregnancy will do well to learn all of the facts before reaching a decision. For example, donor insemination should not be used to shore up a shaky marriage. The birth of a child which is not the husband's may add to the strain.

The donor should be anonymous, of high fertility, excellent health, good intelligence, and free from hereditary diseases. If possible he should have characteristics resembling those of the husband, and have a blood grouping and Rh factor compatible with those of the wife. In some cases the physician insists that the husband adopt the baby to protect it against a later question of legitimacy.

Counseling

Before or after marriage it is sometimes difficult for the couple to find a specialist qualified to give help with contraception or fertility questions or problems. The Planned Parenthood Federation of America (see end of this chapter) will identify a qualified physician or point out the nearest planned parenthood center where advice about these matters as well as advice in other phases of marriage can be obtained directly or by referral.

some national organizations that provide or recommend marriage counseling services

American Association of Marriage Counselors, Inc., 27 Woodcliff Drive, Madison, New Jersey.

American Group Psychotherapy Association, 1790 Broadway, New York, New York 10019.

American Psychiatric Association, 1700 18 Street, N. W., Washington, D. C.

American Psychological Association, 1333 16 Street, N. W., Washington, D. C.

American Social Health Association, 1790 Broadway, New York, New York 10028.

Child Study Association of America, 9 East 89 Street, New York, New York 10019.

Family Service Association of America, 215 Park Avenue, New York, New York 10003.

Maternity Center Association, 48 East 92 Street, New York, New York 10028.

National Council on Family Relations, 1219 University Avenue, S. E., Minneapolis, Minnesota.

Planned Parenthood Federation of America, 515 Madison Avenue, New York, New York 10022.

Society for the Scientific Study of Sex, 12 East 41 Street, New York, New York 10017.

selected further reading by chapter and subject

The numbers in parentheses refer to the source as it is numbered in the annotated list on pages 196 to 217.

CHAPTER IV:

preparation for marriage

selected further reading   annotated

1. Ackerman, Nathan, *The Psychodynamics of Family Life*. New York:
    Basic Books, Inc., 1958. 379 pages.

    A classic, psychoanalytically-oriented and sometimes difficult presen-
    tation of the interdependence of individual and family action. The
    author, a pioneer in family therapy, documents his presentation
    with extensive case material from his files and introduces the reader
    to family therapy procedures as well as to family interaction theory.
    The chapter on parental roles contains a valuable discussion of
    motivations for having children.

2. Anshen, Ruth Nanda, ed., *The Family: Its Function and Destiny*, rev.
    ed. New York: Harper & Row, Publishers, 1954. 538 pages.

    The book is in two parts, anthropological and sociological. Part I
    consists of a series of articles on types of family life across the
    world; Part II of articles on the structure, functions, and crises of
    the American family.

3. Baruch, Dorothy W., *New Ways in Sex Education*. New York: Mc-
    Graw-Hill Book Company, 1959. 256 pages.

    A psychoanalytically influenced guide for parents and teachers.
    The author, a noted child analyst, draws on classroom, clinic, and
    family illustrations to elaborate her thesis that sex education is not
    a matter of facts but of feelings. Good sex education, she believes,
    helps children to develop the capacity to love. She includes some
    general suggestions for giving this broader sex education to children
    and adolescents, but hopes that readers will select from these sug-

gestions on the basis of their own feelings and experiences and not treat them as prescriptions to swallow whole.

4. Baruch, Dorothy W., *Parents Can Be People*. New York: Appleton-Century-Crofts, 1944. 262 pages.

A book to reassure parents. The author asserts that parents may not always enjoy their parental roles and that this need not be damaging to children unless parents try to hide their feelings from themselves. The World War II publishing date makes some of the illustrative material appear dated, but the book remains valuable in its understanding of the range of feelings of normal parents toward their children.

5. Bell, Norman W. and Ezra F. Vogel, eds., *A Modern Introduction to the Family*. New York: Free Press of Glencoe, Inc., 1960. 691 pages.

For advanced students. This is a collection of articles by outstanding scholars dealing with the relation between the family and internal processes, external systems, and personality. The compilers provide a framework for a functional analysis of the family—task performance, family leadership, integration and solidarity, and pattern maintenance.

6. Bettelheim, Bruno, *Dialogues with Mothers*. New York: Free Press of Glencoe, Inc., 1962. 216 pages.

The author discusses transcriptions of round table discussions with a group of young mothers about how to raise their children. He leads the group to consider why a child might have behaved in a particular way, and why the child's mother might have chosen to respond as she did.

7. Bieber, Irving *et al.*, *Homosexuality: A Psychoanalytic Study*. New York: Basic Books, Inc., 1962. 358 pages.

A clinical and statistical study comparing male homosexuals and male heterosexuals in psychoanalytic treatment. The researchers conclude that homosexuals are born heterosexual, but acquire a fear of heterosexuality during childhood. Homosexuality is an adaptive mechanism and homosexuals retain their capacity for heterosexual development. The study makes use of family interaction concepts relating to personality development and suggests that male homosexuality is most apt to arise where the mother is seductive and the father is hostile and aloof. The first chapter, on concepts of male homosexuality, is a thorough review of the basic literature on homosexuality.

8. Bossard, James H. and Eleanor Stoker Boll, *One Marriage, Two Faiths*. New York: The Ronald Press Company, 1957. 180 pages.

A sympathetic but realistic account by two sociologists of the pros and cons of mixed marriages. The authors stress that a marriage need not cut across major faith lines to be mixed. Members of differing national or denominational subgroupings of a single faith—e.g., an Irish and an Italian Roman Catholic, or a Baptist and an Episcopalian—may also experience the problems of a mixed marriage. The authors claim that mixed marriages are subject to greater strain than other marriages and for that reason should be entered into with mature caution. They do not suggest, however, that mixed marriages are always unsuccessful. A final chapter describes the forms some stable mixed marriages have taken.

9. Bossard, James H. and Eleanor Stoker Boll, *Ritual in Family Living*. Philadelphia: University of Pennsylvania Press, 1950. 228 pages.

The authors point out that even couples of the same social class are apt to bring to marriage variant expectations of what constitutes good family life. Local or nationality backgrounds may color their expectations, as well as their experiences growing up in the unique patterns of their own families. The authors suggest that the daily rituals of family life that become habitual and automatic during the growing-up years become deeply rooted in one's personality and that reasoning alone may not suffice to handle the emotional conflicts arising where marital partners' family habits and values are at variance. Where marriages cross social class lines as well, these problems are compounded.

10. Burgess, Ernest W. and Paul Wallin with Gladys D. Schultz, *Courtship, Engagement and Marriage*. Philadelphia: J. B. Lippincott Co., 1953. 444 pages.

A popular edition of a research report investigating factors that contribute to marital success and failure. The authors predicted the marital success of 1000 engaged couples and conducted follow-up evaluations of 666 of these couples, from three to five years after marriage. They found three factors as pivotal for marital success: (1) love and display of affection (2) sex and (3) emotional dependence of spouses upon each other. On the basis of their findings they have devised the Burgess-Wallin Engagement Success and Marriage Prediction Schedules, samples of which are included, and the components of which are discussed. They also include a survey of the changing mores surrounding American dating and courtship. Comments by the couples studied with regard to dating, the engagement period, and marital adjustment are also quoted.

11. Buxton, C. Lee and Anna L. Southam, *Human Infertility*, with a chapter on endometrial diagnosis by Earl T. Engle. New York: Harper & Row, Publishers, Hoeber Medical Division, 1958. 229 pages.

    An explanation of the causes and treatment of infertility. The authors consider the couple rather than a single marital partner to be the diagnostic and therapeutic unit and are concerned with psychological and sociological as well as physiological factors related to infertility. The text is detailed and comprehensive but written simply enough for the advanced nonmedical as well as the medical reader.

12. Calderone, Mary Steichen, ed. *Abortion in the United States*. New York: Harper & Row, Publishers, Hoeber Medical Division, 1958. 224 pages.

    Report of a conference sponsored by the Planned Parenthood Federation of America. The report contains the papers of distinguished speakers on illegal and therapeutic abortion as a medical, legal, social, and psychiatric problem. The factual material is current and provocative and includes descriptions by Scandinavian representatives of abortion practices in their countries and digests of abortion laws and statistics in the United States. The report also contains the stenographic recordings of the frank discussion from the floor which followed each speaker's presentation.

13. Corner, George W., *The Hormones in Human Reproduction*. Princeton: Princeton University Press, 1947. 281 pages.

    A comprehensive description of the role of hormonal activity in human reproduction. Topics include comparative animal and human hormonal activity and the nature and functions of the male and female hormones. The author introduces his material with a review of the reproductive system and relates each hormonal activity to the total activity of the system.

14. Cory, Donald Webster, *The Homosexual in America*. New York: Chilton Company, Book Division, 1953. 326 pages.

    An account of the sociology and the psychology of homosexuality, written by a practicing homosexual. The book describes what it feels like to be a homosexual and to live in the homosexual community. The author claims that homosexuality is a natural, inherent, compulsive, and virtually nonreversible drive.

15. Dickinson, Robert Latou, *Human Sex Anatomy: A Topographical Hand Atlas.* Baltimore: The Williams & Wilkins Company, 1949. 145 pages, 175 figures.

An atlas of male and female sexual anatomy written for medical and allied personnel. The text and commentary introducing the atlas are written in a technical style. This liability is compensated for by the finely executed drawings of the atlas proper. They are extensive, detailed, and illustrative of the variation of male and female sexual anatomy. Drawings are also included of the anatomy of contraception and of the routes of the sperm and the ovum in fertilization.

16. Dick-Read, Grantly, *Childbirth without Fear,* rev. ed. New York: Harper & Row, Publishers, 1953. 298 pages.

The classic text on "natural childbirth." The author considers the fear-tension-pain syndrome to be the source of excessive discomfort in normal labor and delivery, and suggests a threefold program of education to combat the fears of childbirth. This program includes education in the physiology of reproduction, in the dynamics of the fear-tension-pain syndrome, and in prenatal exercises, including relaxation methods. Attention is given also to the importance of emotional support at childbirth, to breast-feeding, and to the role of the husband during pregnancy and at childbirth.

17. Dobzhansky, Theodosius, *Evolution, Genetics and Man.* New York: John Wiley & Sons, Inc., 1955. 398 pages.

A concise, well-illustrated account of man's biological evolution, written by a well-known geneticist. The approach utilizes material from zoology, botany, physical anthropology and genetics. Chapters discuss the hereditary transmission of genes, the interplay of heredity with such environmental factors as natural selection and adaptation, the development of populations, races and species, and the historical record of organic evolution including human evolution.

18. Duvall, Evelyn Millis, *Facts of Life and Love for Teenagers.* New York: Association Press, 1950. 254 pages.

A sympathetic and candid guide for teenagers. The author discusses physical maturation, dating, love, courtship, and preparation for marriage. She takes up the everyday problems of growing up, as well as broad developmental themes, and discusses frankly such deviant phenomena as homosexuality, prostitution, VD, and falling in love with those already married.

19. Eastman, Nicholsen J., *Expectant Motherhood,* 3rd ed. Boston: Little, Brown & Company, 1957. 198 pages.

A handbook for the pregnant woman. The author describes the signs and symptoms of pregnancy, the growth and development of the fetus, diet and hygiene in pregnancy, common discomforts and their treatment, danger signals, preparations for the baby, the birth of the baby, "painless childbirth," and convalescence. The style is simple and matter-of-fact, stressing the normalcy of pregnancy without oversimplifying its problems.

20. Eckert, Ralph G., *Sex Attitudes in the Home.* New York: Association Press, 1956. 172 pages.

A warm, informal guide for parents. The author stresses that sex education is not a matter of providing answers but of helping children to acquire healthy attitudes. He describes the development of love-sex feelings during the early, pre-adolescent and adolescent years and suggests ways in which parents can help their children during these periods. A final chapter provides some sex education for parents themselves.

21. Ehrmann, Winston, *Premarital Dating Behavior.* New York: Holt, Rinehart & Winston, Inc., 1954. 316 pages.

The report of a research study investigating premarital dating behavior and sexual activity on a large coeducational campus. The data suggest a conflict in male and female collegiate sex standards. A significant number of males engaged in premarital sexual relations with female students. Most of these men, however, did not engage in sexual relationships with girls in whom they were emotionally interested and did not engage in sexual relationships during the engagement period. Fewer females engaged in premarital sexual activity. However, a significant number of females indicated that they would consider premarital sexual relations with fiancés but not with any other men.

22. Eisenstein, Victor W., ed., *Neurotic Interaction in Marriage.* New York: Basic Books, Inc., 1956. 352 pages.

A collection of articles on neurotic marital interaction, written for the advanced student or professional reader. Marital relationships are discussed clinically, in terms of diagnosis, prognosis, and treatment. Topics include neurotic choice of a mate, reciprocal neurotic patterns and the effect of chronic marital discord on children. Legal and research aspects of marital interaction also are discussed. Many of the articles are of the psychoanalytic school. Others make specific recommendations for the marriage counselor, the group therapist, and the family case worker.

23. Ellis, Albert and Albert Abarbanel, eds., *The Encyclopedia of Sexual Behavior*. New York: Hawthorn Books, Inc., 1961. 2 vols.

A collection of articles by outstanding writers in the field. Topics cover three broad categories: (1) sex anatomy and physiology (2) social and psychological aspects of sex and (3) love, marriage and the family. It makes available basic articles on specialized as well as general topics related to sexual behavior. The following articles are illustrative: "Abstinence" by Hugo Berjil, "Advances in Modern Sex Research" by Leo Chall, "Autoeroticism" by Lester Dearborn and "Prostitution" by Harry Benjamin.

24. English, O. Spurgeon and Constance J. Foster, *Fathers Are Parents Too*. New York: G. P. Putnam's Sons, 1951. 304 pages.

A text for fathers, written by a psychoanalytically oriented psychiatrist. The author describes in a warm and informal style, the developmental stages and the needs of children from birth through adolescence, and suggests how fathers may play a significant role in their children's healthy development during each of these stages. Attention is also paid to the special problems of the first-time father, the stepfather, the adoptive father, and the grandfather.

25. English, O. Spurgeon and Gerald H. J. Pearson, *Emotional Problems of Living: Avoiding the Neurotic Pattern*, rev. ed. New York: W. W. Norton & Company, Inc., 1955. 438 pages.

A psychoanalytically oriented introduction to personality development, written for workers in interpersonal fields. The authors describe the development of personality chronologically, concentrating on the periods from birth through adolescence, but giving attention also to marital, work, and old age adjustments. Chapters discussing normal personality development through the oral, anal, phallic, latent, and adolescent stages, are followed by discussions of emotional disturbances that may occur during these formative periods. The authors also discuss common neurotic patterns as manifested in the adult and describe typical methods of treating them.

26. Fishbein, Morris, ed., *Children for the Childless*. New York: Doubleday & Company, Inc., 1954. 223 pages.

A clear and readable discussion of medical, emotional, and social factors relating to infertility. Experts discuss such topics as: physical and psychosomatic aspects of fertility and infertility, treatment procedures for infertility, artificial insemination, adoption, the nature of heredity, and contemporary parenthood.

27. Fishbein, Morris and Ruby Jo Reeves Kennedy, eds., *Modern Marriage and Family Living*. New York: Oxford University Press, 1957. 545 pages.

For the beginning reader, a basic and interdisciplinary collection of articles on marriage and family life. The book is divided into five parts: (1) Social Aspects of Marriage (2) Preparation for Marriage (3) Marriage (4) Conception, Pregnancy, and Childbirth and (5) The Child in the Family. The contributors are well known in family-life circles, and the collection as a whole constitutes a good introductory survey.

28. Flanagan, Geraldine Lux, *The First Nine Months of Life*. New York: Simon and Schuster, Inc., 1962. 95 pages.

A simple, scientifically accurate account in words and photographs, of the development of the human organism from egg cell to birth. The author describes the changing form of the fetus month by month and illustrates her narrative with photographs from an outstanding research collection.

29. Foote, Nelson N. and Leonard S. Cottrell, *Identity and Interpersonal Competence*. Chicago: University of Chicago Press, 1955. 305 pages.

The authors believe that interpersonal competence is the critical variable in marital stability. They criticize research which stresses trait homogeneity as a critical factor in marital stability, for disregarding the dynamic and changing nature of human behavior. Under interpersonal competence they discuss health, intelligence, empathy, autonomy, judgment, and creativity, and suggest hypotheses for measuring the weight of each of these factors in family life. They also suggest ways in which family-serving agencies may use their facilities to further research in this area.

30. Ford, Clellan S. and Frank A. Beach, *Patterns of Sexual Behavior*. New York: Harper & Row, Publishers, 1951. 307 pages.

A study of sexual behavior in cross-cultural human groups and in other mammalian groups. Topics include precoital and coital behavior in these groups and also homosexual and self-stimulatory behaviors. Biological heredity and life experiences are viewed as contributing jointly to sexual forms. Human sexuality is so malleable to cultural conditioning, however, that biological capacities may become obscured.

31. Fraiberg, Selma, *The Magic Years: Understanding and Handling the Problems of Early Childhood*. New York: Charles Scribner's Sons, 1959. 305 pages.

   An analysis of personality development during the first five years of life. The author is influenced by the findings of Piaget and of the ego psychologists. She stresses the importance of understanding the mental life of the preschool child when trying to help him deal with the everyday problems of growing up. She states that it is not the presence of problems which makes or breaks his healthy development, but how he is helped to cope with conflicts, challenges, and frustrations when they do arise.

32. Freedman, Ronald, Pascal K. Whelpton, and Arthur A. Campbell, *Family Planning, Sterility and Population Growth*. New York: Mc-Graw-Hill Book Company, 1959. 515 pages.

   A study of fecundity, family planning, and preferred family size in a major American population sample. Study results suggest that family limitation is nearly universally approved in the United States, that social classes are coming to share a common preference for the two to four child family, and that, if present family growth patterns continue, the American population will grow rapidly to the point of forcing major social change. The basic content of the book is written in nontechnical language for the nonspecialist reader. Appendices provide technical notes on sampling methods and interpretations for the advanced reader.

33. Fromm, Erich, *The Art of Loving*. New York: Harper & Row, Publishers, 1956. 133 pages.

   Love is defined as active concern for the life and growth of the love object. Its basic components are care, responsibility, respect, and knowledge. The author distinguishes love so defined from romantic love, and discusses parental love, brotherly love, erotic love, self-love, and love of God, in relation to it. He suggests ways one can begin to practice the art and discipline of mature love, but warns also, that many factors in our culture impede the development of mature love.

34. Genne, William H., *Husbands and Pregnancy*. New York: Association Press, 1956. 127 pages.

   A handbook for expectant fathers. The author describes the physical and emotional changes wives may experience during pregnancy, and the changes that may occur in their households after the baby arrives. He views pregnancy as a family affair and emphasizes the emotional support that the husband should give to his wife during pregnancy and immediately afterwards.

35. Gould, Joan, *Will My Baby Be Born Normal?* New York: The Public Affairs Committee, Inc., 1958. Public Affairs Pamphlet No. 272. 20 pages.

A concise description of the causes of abnormality in infants, of the preventive measures that may sometimes be taken, and of the medical and social assistance available to parents of exceptional children.

36. Gray, Henry, *Anatomy of the Human Body.* 27th ed. Philadelphia: Lea & Febiger, 1959. 1458 pages.

The classic text on anatomy. An introductory chapter gives a breakdown of the various divisions of anatomy and definitions of important general terms. Subsequent chapters describe each major system of the body in detail. The section on embryology has been extensively revised. The chapters on the urinogenital system and on the ductless glands are also excellent. Each chapter is profusely illustrated.

37. Gruenberg, Sidonie Matsner, *The Wonderful Story of How You Were Born.* New York: Doubleday & Company, Inc., Garden City Books, 1952. 39 pages.

An illustrated account for young children of how life begins. The author speaks directly to the child's curiosity and explains how egg and sperm unite and grow into a baby. She compares animal and human parents and describes the changes that will take place in the new baby's body as he grows and becomes ready to be a parent.

38. Guttmacher, Alan F., *Babies by Choice or by Chance.* New York: Doubleday & Company, Inc., 1959. 289 pages.

A good general introduction to the many subjects included in the broad category of family planning. Birth prevention methods and problems relating to infertility are discussed as well as the specialized topics of sterilization, abortion (therapeutic and criminal), artificial insemination, and eugenics. The author has the faculty of explaining technical material clearly.

39. Guttmacher, Alan F., *Pregnancy and Birth: A Book for Expectant Parents.* New York: The Viking Press, Inc., 1956. 335 pages.

Probably the most complete book on pregnancy and childbirth written for the layman. Beginning with the process of fertilization and the reproductive anatomy of both sexes, it deals, in a manner both comprehensive and interesting, with the diagnosis of pregnancy, the progress of fetal life, modern improvements in prenatal care and in the conduct of delivery, the stages of labor, twinning, and postpartum care of both mother and infant. While including careful consideration of the major complications of and special procedures involved in abnormal pregnancies and births, the author inspires confidence by repeatedly stressing the competence of modern medicine and the normalcy of the majority of pregnancies. He offers his own generally liberal views on obstetrical issues, but also supplies alternative views, often provides a brief historical perspective, and in all matters defers to the choice of the patient's own physician. "Highly recommended" by the Journal of the American Medical Association.

40. Guttmacher, Alan F. and the editors of Consumer Reports, *The Consumers Union Report on Family Planning*. New York: Consumers Union of U. S., 1962. 145 pages.

An up-to-date guide to family planning, written in two parts. Part I compares contraceptive methods and products, including the newest oral contraceptives (the "pill"). Part II discusses current methods of improving fertility. Among the valuable features are consumer ratings of standard contraceptive brand names and a list of agencies offering family planning assistance. Illustrations of contraceptives are also included.

41. Hamilton, Eleanor L., "Emotional Factors in Pregnancy: An Intensive Study of 14 Normal Primaparae." Unpublished Ph.D. Dissertation, Teachers College, Columbia University, 1955. 370 pages.

A detailed account of the feelings experienced by fourteen women during their first pregnancies. The researcher reports their emotional views on learning of their pregnancy, on the pleasures, discomforts, and fears experienced during pregnancy and on labor and delivery, breastfeeding and the postnatal period. Many quotations as well as stenographic accounts of the subjects' verbalizations during labor and delivery are included.

42. Hunt, Morton M., *Her Infinite Variety*. New York: Harper & Row, Publishers, 1962. 333 pages.

An engaging argument in praise of the many-sided modern woman. The author acknowledges that contemporary society urges many contradictory roles on women, some of which seem to jeopardize their femininity. He suggests, however, that the solution is not to be found in a return to traditional female roles. He feels that the woman of the future will choose complexity over simplicity and maintain several roles simultaneously. He finds this woman in the minority today, but urges her on—liking her enormously.

43. Hunt, Morton M., *The Natural History of Love*. New York: Alfred A. Knopf, Inc., 1959. 416 pages.

An engaging history of the emotional relationships between men and women, from the time of the Greeks to the present. The author points out that the word "love" has had many meanings throughout history, and documents his point richly from diaries, private correspondences, books of domestic conduct, court gossip, and the like.

44. Katz, Myer, "Connotative Meaning as a Variable in Marital Success and Discord." Unpublished Ph.D. Dissertation, Teachers College, Columbia University, 1959. 82 pages.

A research study supporting the thesis that similarity of semantic concepts between marriage partners contributes to marital happiness. The researcher sorted the meanings given by twenty happily and twenty unhappily married couples to a list of concepts, some relevant to marriage (e.g., "love," "sex relations," and "responsibility") and some nonrelevant (e.g., "mosquito," "sand" and "elbow"). Unhappily married couples were more at variance in their over-all meanings than happy couples and especially so in the meanings they assigned to marriage-related concepts. The researcher suggests the relevance of this finding to communication problems in marriage.

45. Kavinoky, Nadine, "Premarital Medical Examination" in Clark Vincent, ed., *Readings in Marriage Counseling*. New York: Thomas Y. Crowell Company, 1957, pp. 126-33.

The author points out that the premarital physician sees a young couple at a moment of both anticipation and apprehension of sexual love. She suggests what a good premarital examination should include and how the physican might use it to provide them with a good educational experience regarding sex.

46. Kinsey, Alfred C., Wardell B. Pomeroy, and Clyde E. Martin, *Sexual Behavior in the Human Male*. Philadelphia: W. B. Saunders Company, 1948. 804 pages.

Kinsey, Alfred C., Wardell B. Pomeroy, Clyde E. Martin, and Paul H. Gebhard, *Sexual Behavior in the Human Female*. Philadelphia: W. B. Saunders Company, 1953. 842 pages.

The most comprehensive studies to date of American sexual behavior. Topics include types and comparisons of male and female sexual behavior, and factors affecting sexual outlet. The history and research methods of the studies are also reported. The orientation of the studies is quantitative and behavioristic.

47. Kirkendall, Lester A., *Too Young to Marry?* New York: Public Affairs Committee, Inc., 1956. Public Affairs Pamphlet No. 236. 28 pages.

The author discusses the trend toward early marriages and the social factors, such as prolonged education, that make it difficult for mature young couples to marry when ready. He recognizes, however, that the arguments and motivations for early marriage are not equally valid and makes the following suggestions: (1) that society assist mature young people to marry when they are ready (2) that it help them to decide how ready they are and (3) that couples approach early marriage with caution.

48. Kirkpatrick, Clifford, *The Family as Process and Institution.* New York: The Ronald Press Company, 1955. 651 pages.

A comprehensive text on marriage and family life. The author, a sociologist, presents family life as a series of dramas within an institutionalized structure and a changing social scene. He reviews the alternatives open to members in typical family dramas and examines possible outcomes. He provides no neat solutions, but rather an understanding of the inevitable combination of gratification, frustration, and long-term effects.

49. Krich, A. M., ed., *Women: The Variety and Meaning of Their Sexual Experience,* introduction by Margaret Mead. New York: Dell Books, 1953. 319 pages.

Krich, A. M., ed., *Men: The Variety and Meaning of Their Sexual Experience,* introduction by Margaret Mead. New York: Dell Books, 1954. 319 pages.

Companion volumes of articles by pioneer and contemporary authorities. The contributors discuss sexual functioning and deviant sexual behavior in each major life phase. The articles in both volumes correspond, reporting the views of what 100 women and 100 men think is wrong with their marriages.

50. LeMasters, E. E., *Modern Courtship and Marriage.* New York: The Macmillan Company, 1957. 619 pages.

An introductory textbook on the sociology of American marriage, including a lengthy analysis of our courtship system and its social problems.

51. Levine, Lena and Beka Doherty, *The Menopause*. New York: Random House, 1952. 98 pages.

    The physical changes in the body during menopause and the effect of mental attitudes on menopause. Modern women, the authors suggest, adjust to menopause with unprecedented ease because of their greater acceptance of their bodies and greater awareness of their capacities beyond childbearing.

52. Levine, Milton I. and Jean H. Seligmann, *A Baby Is Born*. New York: Golden Press, Inc., 1949. 52 pages.

    A story (for children six to ten) of how a baby begins, grows in its mother's body and is born. It is attractively and extensively illustrated and is written simply enough for some children to read themselves.

53. Levine, Milton I. and Jean H. Seligmann, *The Wonder of Life*. New York: Golden Press, Inc., 1952. 116 pages.

    A book for older children describing simply but carefully the creation of life in the animal and human worlds. It contains clear diagrams of the physiology of human reproduction and a good glossary of sexual terms.

54. Levy, John and Ruth Munroe, *The Happy Family*. New York: Alfred A. Knopf, Inc., 1938. 319 pages.

    A classic account of normal marriage and family life. The authors discuss how families begin and develop into going concerns, noting in the process typical adjustments and vicissitudes experienced along the way. They illustrate extensively from normal family histories. The prewar publishing date does not detract from the book's merit and charm; for example, the description of the range of moods and behaviors typical in a healthy sexual relationship continues to be one of the most widely quoted.

55. Mace, David R., *What Is Marriage Counseling?* New York: The Public Affairs Committee, Inc., 1957. Public Affairs Pamphlet No. 250. 28 pages.

    A concise description of premarital, marital, and divorce counseling, of the qualifications of properly trained marriage counselors, of the ways in which they work with couples, and of the ways in which couples can help in their own counseling.

56. Maternity Center Association, *A Baby Is Born,* 2nd ed. New York: The Maternity Center Association, 1960. 66 pages.

A picture story of conception, of the development of the baby in its mother's body, of the changes in the mother's body during pregnancy, and of the progress of normal and breech labor and delivery. The text is clear, and the illustrations, many of them photographs of clay models by a physician-sculptor team, are outstanding.

57. Maternity Center Association, *Work Conference on the Childbearing Needs of Families in a Changing World.* New York: The Maternity Center Association, 1962. 104 pages.

A condensed compilation of the papers and work-group reports of an interdisciplinary conference on childbearing families. The papers focus on emotional needs and physical care in childbearing, and reflect the growing trends toward family-centered maternity care.

58. Mead, Margaret, *Male and Female.* New York: William Morrow & Company, Inc., 1949. 477 pages.

A panoramic and provocative survey of sex-roles by a well-known anthropologist. Utilizing field data from the South Seas and urban North America, the author pursues the thesis that while biologically inherited characteristics are significant in personality development, cultures traditionally have divided sex roles too sharply and deprived their members of exercising their full capacities. The author deplores the exclusion of American women from participation in their own childbirth experiences and the discouragement given them regarding breast-feeding their infants.

59. Michigan, State of, *Report of the Governor's Study Commission on the Deviated Criminal Sex Offender.* Lansing, Michigan, 1951. 245 pages.

The report distinguishes between sex deviants and sex offenders and tries to set policy to provide protection for society and compassion for the individual offender. It does not equate sex crime with mental illness as defined legally, but does see it as a symptom of emotional disturbance which needs psychiatric understanding and rehabilitation. It also focuses on the sex crime victim and recommends preventive mental health measures as the best protection against sex crime.

60. Mudd, Emily, *et al.*, eds., *Marriage Counseling: A Casebook*. New York: Association Press, 1958. 488 pages.

A casebook published by the American Association of Marriage Counselors. Association members of various counseling persuasions describe premarital and marital adjustment, divorce counseling and counseling of the unmarried, as they have conducted these in their own practices. Articles are also included on marriage in the United States today, on the principles, processes and techniques of marriage counseling, and on the purposes and functions of the American Association of Marriage Counselors.

61. Murdock, George Peter, *Social Structure*. New York: The Macmillan Company, 1949. 387 pages.

The classic refutation of Westermarck's thesis that the nuclear family is the most evolved and best family structure. Drawing on the Yale University Human Relations Area Files, the author points out that both preliterate and literate societies share the same regularities and principles of social structure. The structures themselves vary, however, and while the nuclear family is a universal unit, only in a minority of cases is it independent. More typically, clusters of nuclear families aggregate into polygamous or extended family groupings.

62. National Academy of Sciences, Committee of Science and Public Policy, *The Growth of World Population*. Washington, D. C.: National Academy of Sciences—National Research Council, Publication 1091, 1963. 38 pages.

The report of a panel of experts that deals with biomedical aspects and social and economic factors of population growth. A succinct discussion of steps in the conception process that might be interrupted or manipulated to limit family size—and of present and future techniques to accomplish this.

63. Newman, Horatio Hackett, *Multiple Human Births*. New York: Doubleday & Company, Inc., 1940. 214 pages.

A popular account, by a specialist, of the causes, frequencies, and distinguishing features of twins and other multiple birth siblings. Discussion also of the interplay of hereditary and environmental factors in the development of multiple birth siblings and review of a number of studies on heredity and environment issues using twin subjects. Among the studies is the author's report of observed differences and similarities in twenty pairs of identical twins reared separately from infancy.

64. Newton, Niles, *Maternal Emotions*. New York: Harper & Row, Publishers, Hoeber Medical Division, 1955. 140 pages.

A report of a research study suggesting that women's feelings about menstruation, sexual intercourse, pregnancy, childbirth, breastfeeding, infant care, and societal roles for men and women are significantly correlated. The section on breast-feeding is especially well done and that on discrepancies between biological and cultural femininity is also of interest.

65. Pilpel, Harriet F. and Theodora Zavin, *Your Marriage and the Law*. New York: Holt, Rinehart & Winston, Inc., 1952. 385 pages.

A discussion of the legal aspects of marriage by lawyers who have a facility for making technical material lucid and enjoyable. Topics include medical as well as social factors relating to marriage, e.g., medical requisites for getting a marriage license, legal factors in birth control, artificial insemination, abortion and sterilization, and sex and the criminal law. The authors illustrate each of these legal issues with examples from court annals.

66. Pike, James A., *If You Marry Outside Your Faith*. New York: Harper & Row, Publishers, 1954. 191 pages.

The author, an Episcopal bishop, urges that couples contemplating interfaith marriage engage in serious study of their own religious attitudes before making a final decision. He suggests that many couples find such study leading them to a common religious position. He suggests further that where divergence continues, the wisest course may be not to marry.

67. Planned Parenthood Federation of America, *To Those Denied a Child*. New York: Planned Parenthood Federation of America, n.d. 19 pages.

A brief, simple summary of the major physiological reasons for childlessness, and the recommended procedures for diagnosis and treatment, including addresses of especially equipped hospitals and clinics. Without going into details, or promising success in the majority of cases, the pamphlet stresses the necessity of (1) examination and/or treatment for both spouses (2) the husband's examination preceding his wife's and (3) strict adherence to the physician's directions.

68. Portnoy, Louis and Jules Sallman, *Fertility in Marriage: A Guide for the Childless*. New York: Farrar, Strauss & Company, 1950. 250 pages.

On the basic questions and concerns of childless couples. The authors describe conception, physical and emotional factors impeding it, and procedures to help couples have children. They also discuss artificial insemination and adoption. Appendices list infertility services and adoption centers in each state.

69. Potter, Edith Louise, *Fundamentals of Human Reproduction*. New York: McGraw-Hill Book Company, 1948. 231 pages.

A clear and readable introduction to the development of the human organism until birth. Early chapters describe simple cell division, its elaboration in human reproduction, the role of inheritance in the formation of body pattern, and the role of the sex organs in reproduction. Later chapters describe the development of the embryo, the formation of the placenta, the development of the growing fetus and the elaboration of its organs and body framework. A final chapter describes the birth process and the first adjustments of the newly born child to the extrauterine environment. Each chapter is richly illustrated, including, for example, photographs of the embryo and fetus in relation to the uterus and placenta at successive stages of development, and drawings of the proportionate increase in size of the growing fetus from age fourteen days to full-term.

70. Pryor, Karen, *Nursing Your Baby*. New York: Harper & Row, Publishers, 1963. 274 pages.

Written by a young mother for young mothers, this is an articulate lay discussion of breast-feeding, its history, suggested preparations for women during pregnancy, doctors' attitudes pro and con, medications *not* to take during labor that would inhibit the milk "letdown," the nutrient content of human milk, the psychological benefits to both mother and child, differences in feeding babies of different ages up to eighteen months, and the need of young nursing mothers for each other's support.

71. Rainwater, Lee, *And the Poor Get Children*. Chicago: Quadrangle Books, Inc., 1960. 202 pages.

The findings of investigation of family planning practices in white and Negro lower socioeconomic groups. The summary finding is that psychological and social forces within lower income groups, rather than the mechanical aspects of contraceptive usage, are responsible for the low success of family planning in these populations. Quotations from the interview data make the report provocative.

72. Richman, T. Lefay, *Venereal Disease: Old Plague—New Challenge.* New York: Public Affairs Committee, Inc., 1960. Public Affairs Pamphlet No. 292. 20 pages.

A concise survey of the recent history of venereal disease. Emphasis is on increasing incidence of venereal disease and the medical and social measures being taken to combat it, especially among teenagers.

73. Scheinfeld, Amram, *The New You and Heredity.* Philadelphia: J. B. Lippincott Company, 1950. 616 pages.

A popular and profusely illustrated introduction to human genetics. The author describes the process of gene transmission, including in detail the transmission of physical attributes, IQ potentialities, special talents and genetic abnormalities. Evolution, race and eugenics are also considered. One chapter consists of do-it-yourself charts for predicting what—or whom—one's own unborn children may look like.

74. Scheinfeld, Amram, *Women and Men.* London: Chatto & Windus, Ltd., 947. 394 pages.

A popularized account of the biological differences between men and women and the effect on their behavior patterns and social role divisions. The author describes the development of each sex from conception to maturity, and discusses differences between men and women in physical and emotional stamina, susceptibility to illness, aptitude and achievement patterns, and dominance and submission tendencies. He believes that both heredity and environment are important factors in sex-role considerations and applies his findings to the problems of sex-role division of labor, marriage and family life, and women's rights.

75. Stone, Hannah M. and Abraham Stone, *A Marriage Manual.* New York: Simon and Schuster, Inc., 1953. 301 pages.

A nontechnical but comprehensive introduction to physical and emotional factors in sex and reproduction. The chapters—in a question and answer form for easy reference—discuss the physiology of the male and female sex organs, fertility, infertility and reproduction, contraception, and sexual pleasure in marriage. Those on the structure and functions of sex organs are especially thorough.

76. Tharp, Roland G., "Psychological Patterning in Marriage," *Psychological Bulletin*, LX (March 1963), 97-117.

The author reviews the literature concerning marital success and its prediction. He concludes that general personality characteristics, whether like or unlike, are less relevant to marital success than partners' specific role expectations for marriage. These role expectations may be conventional or unique, but the partners must find their mutual expectations coordinate if the marriage is to be harmonious.

77. Thoms, Herbert, *Childbirth with Understanding.* Springfield, Illinois: Charles C Thomas, Publisher, 1962. 98 pages.

The author describes the pioneer efforts at the Yale–New Haven Medical Center to make childbirth a more emotionally satisfying and family-centered experience. He discusses the organization and curricula of their childbirth and parenthood preparation classes, their provisions for emotional support during labor and delivery, the effect of the husband's presence during labor, rooming-in arrangements and procedures, and the increasing usefulness of nurse-midwives both as teachers and as supportive figures during labor. Attention is given also to ways in which the program has been adapted by clinics and by private physicians. Patients' evaluations of the program are also included.

78. Thoms, Herbert, *Understanding Natural Childbirth: A Book for the Expectant Mother.* New York: McGraw-Hill Book Company, 1950. 112 pages.

A picture story of the experiences of a young mother who elects to have her baby "naturally." Topics include her prenatal classes and exercises, the progress of her labor, the birth of her baby, and her routine in a rooming-in suite. The photographs are unposed and taken at Grace–New Haven Hospital, the American pioneer in natural childbirth.

79. *Today's VD Control Program: A Joint Statement by the Association of State and Territorial Health Offices, The American VD Association and the American Social Health Association.* New York: American Social Health Association, 1963. 70 pages.

An annual report which breaks down by communities and states, the national statistics on venereal disease. Information is included on control and educational projects, on the problems of VD detection in an increasingly mobile American society and on VD as a world health problem.

80. Trilling, Lionel, "The Kinsey Report" in *The Liberal Imagination.* New York: The Viking Press, Inc., 1950, pp. 223-42.

The classic essay on Kinsey. Trilling discusses Kinsey's report of sexual behavior in the human male both as a scientific treatise and as a cultural phenomenon. He concludes that to deal with affective material quantitatively is a typically American procedure and also that quantitative analysis can lead to scientific as well as social over-simplification. The author deplores the impression created by such studies that frequent sexuality is good sexuality, to the neglect of qualitative aspects.

81. Vincent, Clark E., ed., *Readings in Marriage Counseling*. New York: Thomas Y. Crowell Company, 1957. 500 pages.

Authoritative articles by members of contributing fields on the theory and practice of marriage counseling. Symposia from the marriage counseling section of the National Council of Family Relations also are included. Major subjects covered are: (1) Marriage Counseling as an Emerging and Interdisciplinary Profession (2) Premarital Counseling (3) Definitions, Methods and Principles of Marriage Counseling (4) Marriage Counseling with Individuals, Groups, and Couples (5) Theories of Personality Formation and Change Applicable to Marriage Counseling (6) Research in Marriage Counseling and (7) Questions Relating to Marriage Counseling as an Emerging Profession.

82. Vincent, Clark E., *Unmarried Mothers*. New York: Free Press of Glencoe, Inc., 1961. 308 pages.

The first major study of unmarried mothers that includes subjects from all strata of the population, and that compares them with those with no records of illegitimacy. The data suggest that unwed mothers have diverse personality and childhood backgrounds, and that earlier generalizations about unmarried mothers may have been more descriptive of the clientele of specific agencies and physicians than of all unwed mothers. The author suggests that illegitimacy represents an interaction of a person and the kind of society that considers illegitimacy a problem in the first place, and makes the following recommendations: that attention be paid to the pervasive effects of the ambiguous attitudes in American society toward illicit sexual behavior; and that attention be paid to increasing the socially acceptable outlets for girls through which they may experiment during their developmental years, without censure for failure, with their emerging identities.

83. Winch, Robert F., *Mate Selection: A Study of Complementary Needs*. New York: Harper & Row, Publishers, 1958. 350 pages.

The report of a research study investigating complementarity as a factor in mate selection. Statistical and clinical analyses of the interview and TAT responses of a homogeneous sample of twenty-five young middle-class couples suggested that these couples tended to seek out marital partners who were like themselves in their social characteristics, but unlike in their psychological make-up. For example, well-educated but dominant men tended to choose well-educated but submissive wives. The researcher suggests, however, that complementarity may operate in mate selection only in the modern companionate form of marriage, where the marital consorts are expected to be primary sources of emotional support to each other.

84. *The Wolfenden Report: Report of the Committee on Homosexual Offenses and Prostitution.* Authorized American ed., introduction by Karl Menninger. New York: Stein & Day, 1963. 243 pages.

The famous British report on homosexuality and prostitution and their relation to the law. The most controversial recommendation advises that "homosexual behavior between consenting adults, in private, be no longer a criminal offense." The committee did not make this recommendation on psychological grounds, but rather, stressed the legal importance of permitting individual freedom in matters of private morality.

index

A

Abortions, 82-85
  drugs for, 87
  illegal, 85-87
  terms of, explained, 82-84
  in the United States, 84, 85
  and the unwed mother, 86, 87
Adolescent phase, 98-104
  early, 100-102
  and early marriage, 134-135
  homosexuality in, 99, 102, 126
  and hormones, 99, 101
  and interest in the opposite sex, 101
  late, 102-104
  love play in, 101, 103
  masturbation in, 99-103
  menstruation in, 100, 102, 103
  nocturnal emission in, 100, 103
  preadolescence, 98-100
  pregnancy in, 103
  and rebellion, 100
  and secondary sex characteristics, 100
  and sex education, 105-106
  sexual intercourse in, 99, 103
  and society, 106
  and sublimation, 134

Adolescent phase (*Cont.*)
  thrill, 102
  the turn toward heterosexuality, 102
  venereal disease in, 103, 126-127
Adrenal gland and hormone production, 9
Afterbirth, 71
Afterpains, 80
Afterplay, 169-170
Age and marriage, 147-148
Alcoholic, as a prospect for marriage, 146-147
American Association of Marriage Counselors, 161-162, 193
American Group Psychotherapy Association, 193
American Psychiatric Association, 193
American Psychological Association, 193
American Social Health Association, 193
Amniotic sac, 52
Anal phase, 91-93
Anesthesia, and delivery, 78
Antibiotics
  and delivery, 78
  and venereal disease, 122, 124, 127
Anus as the second erotic zone, 91-93

219

Homozygous genes, 58
Hormones
  and the adolescent phase, 99, 101
  estrogen, 9, 15, 20
  female, 2
  FH, 20, 23
  first production of, 2
  FSH, 20, 22, 23
  LH, 20
  male, 2, 9
  and menopause, 26, 27
  and onset of labor, 64
  progesterone, 20
    as a test for pregnancy, 43
  and spontaneous abortions, 83, 84
  synthetic, 15
  testosterone, 9, 10
  therapy, 27
Human chorionic gonadotropin
    (HCG), 43
Hymen, 28-29
  size of, and use of tampons, 29,
    164-165
Hysterectomy, 19

I

Identical twins, 74-76
Identification, of babies, 71
Impotence, 187-188
  from suppressed masturbation, 96
Income and marriage, 152-153
Infants
  anal phase, 91-93
  genital or oedipal phase, 93-96
  oral phase, 90-91
  and sex education, 104-105
  view of sexual relations, 95
Infertility, 187-193
  and artificial insemination, 192
  causes of, 188-189
  counseling for, 192-193
  the extent of, 188
  impotence, 187-188
  premarital examinations for, 190-
    191
  statistics on, 188
Influenza during pregnancy, 56
"Instrument baby," 76
Instruments, use of, in delivery, 76-
  78

Intellect and marriage, 154-155
Interests, personal, and marriage, 143-
    144, 154-155
Intermenstrual phase, 23
Italian pox (*see* Syphilis)

J

Johnson, Samuel (quoted), 157

L

Labia majora, 27
Labia minora, 27-28
Labor (*see also* Delivery)
  and bag of waters, 66-68
  and breech presentations, 76
  and Cesarean section, 78-79
  "false pains," 64
  first (cervical) stage of, 64-68
  and nature of contractions, 64-66
  second stage of, 68-71
  "show," 66
  third stage of, 71-73
  time span of, 63-64
  and use of instruments, 76-78
  and vertex presentations, 76
Lactation (*see* Nursing)
Latent phase, 96-98
LH, 20
Lochia, 80
Love
  capacity for, 146
  in courtship, 146
  and premarital relations, 116-117
  readiness for, 157-159
  romantic, 137, 139-141
  and sexual intercourse, 12
Lubrication
  natural
    in the female, 33-34, 168
    in the male, 13
  and use of condoms, 34

M

Maidenhead (*see* Hymen)
Males
  attitude toward sex organs, 3, 166

Villi, 39, 50
Virginity, the symbol of, 29

W

Warts, venereal, 125
Weight, control of, during pregnancy,
    45
"Wet dreams" (*see* Nocturnal emis-
    sion)
Withdrawal, 13, 179
Women (*see* Females)

X

X chromosome, 1-2
X-rays, and Cesarean section, 78

Y

Y chromosome, 1-2
YMCA, 162

Z

Zygote, formation of, 35, 37